My **FUNCTIONAL** SKILLS

MY **FUNCTIO**

CW00552730

Level 2
Maths
Revision and Exam Practice

Kevin Norley

HODDER
Education

Orders: please contact Hachette UK Distribution, Hely Hutchinson Centre, Milton Road, Didcot, Oxfordshire, OX11 7HH. Telephone: +44 (0)1235 827827. Email education@hachette.co.uk Lines are open from 9 a.m. to 5 p.m., Monday to Friday. You can also order through our website: www.hoddereducation.co.uk

ISBN: 978 1 3983 8701 0

© Kevin Norley 2023

First published in 2023 by
Hodder Education,
An Hachette UK Company
Carmelite House
50 Victoria Embankment
London EC4Y 0DZ

www.hoddereducation.co.uk

Impression number 10 9 8 7 6 5 4 3 2 1

Year   2026 2025 2024 2023

Cover image © Hodder Education

Illustrations by Aptara, Inc.

Typeset in India by Aptara, Inc.

Printed in Spain

A catalogue record for this title is available from the British Library.

Get the most from this book

We all need to decide how to revise in a way that works for us, but learning each topic, testing our understanding and knowing how to answer exam questions is essential.

My Functional Skills will help you to do that in a planned way, topic by topic. Use this book in the way that works best for you: write in it, doodle, personalise your notes; and check your progress by ticking off each section as you revise.

This book is broken down into three sections:

1 Using numbers and the number system
2 Using common measures, shape and space
3 Handling information and data.

Features to help you succeed

DIAGNOSTIC QUESTIONS

Focus! Work out which topics you need to spend more time on by answering these **diagnostic questions**. You can choose to focus on areas where you're weaker and spend less time on the topics you're already really good at.

WORKED EXAMPLE

Oh, so that's how I do it! Every topic includes at least one **worked example** that guides you through the steps to answer an exam-style question.

KEY TERMS

What does that mean? On each page, all the important **key terms** are defined; and there's a handy summary of all of these in the glossary at the back of the book.

EXAM TIP

What *is* the examiner looking for? Throughout the book you'll find **hints and tips** on how to approach answering questions, as well as how you might gain the most marks in the exam.

COMMON MISTAKES

Where did I go wrong? Many of the **common mistakes** and pitfalls students have made in Functional Skills exams are highlighted, so you can avoid making them yourself.

MAKING LINKS

Where can I find out more? Some topics link closely with others. Here you'll see where you can find more information elsewhere in the revision guide that is relevant to the topic.

CHECK YOUR UNDERSTANDING

Now it's my turn! Test your understanding of each topic with these short questions. Review the answers online at www.hoddereducation.co.uk/functional-skills-maths-answers to see whether you have answered correctly.

EXAM-STYLE QUESTIONS

Practice, practice, practice! Get exam-ready by answering these **exam-style questions**. Review the **answers** online at www.hoddereducation.co.uk/functional-skills-maths-answers to see whether you have answered correctly or if you need to try again.

My revision planner

Use this revision planner to plan your revision, topic by topic. Tick each box when you have:

● revised and understood a topic
● tested yourself
● practised exam questions and gone online to check your answers.

1 Using numbers and the number system

2 Using common measures, shape and space

Countdown to my exams

6–8 WEEKS TO GO

○ **What do I need to revise?** Familiarise yourself with the topics you need to revise. You can use the revision planner in this book to help you.

○ **What will the exam look like?** Look at the exam board specification or ask your tutor about the format of your Functional Skills exams. When and where will they take place? How long will they last? What types of questions might you see on the exam papers? The Assessment Breakdown on page 7 gives more information on this.

○ **Get organised.** Organise your notes and make sure you've covered all the topics.

○ **Make a plan.** Create a revision plan that shows the days and times you'll revise each topic. Be realistic – small, focused sessions of around 40–50 minutes will be more achievable and successful. Make sure you allow yourself breaks. Stick to your plan!

2–6 WEEKS TO GO

○ **Make a start.** Use your own revision plan to work through the topics in this book. Look at the explanations, worked examples, key terms, common mistakes and hints and tips. Highlight any important bits and make your own notes in the book if you wish. Tick off each topic when you feel confident, or come back to any topics you think you need to look at again.

○ **What do I know?** Now test your understanding by answering the Check your understanding questions. Look at the answers online at www.hoddereducation.co.uk/functional-skills-maths-answers. What did you get right? Which topics do you need to revisit?

○ **Where do I need help?** Speak to your tutor about any topics you're finding tricky. They may be able to go over them again with you as part of a revision class.

○ **Get exam ready!** The best way to prepare is to practise answering lots and lots of exam questions. Have a go at the exam-style questions in this book and check your answers online at www.hoddereducation.co.uk/functional-skills-maths-answers. Look at and attempt past Functional Skills exam papers – you will find these on your exam board's website, or your tutor will be able to share some with you.

○ **Keep track.** Use the revision planner to keep track of your progress.

1 WEEK TO GO

○ **Have I covered everything?** Check that you have revised every topic on the revision planner. Look at any you haven't already covered; and revisit any topics you still feel less confident about.

○ **Prepare for exam conditions.** Do a complete past exam paper in timed exam conditions to help you plan your time for the real exams. Compare your answers against the mark scheme or ask your tutor to mark it for you.

THE DAY BEFORE

○ **Last-minute check.** Read through your notes and flick through this book to remind yourself of any important points, common mistakes and hints and tips.

○ **When and where is it?** Check the time and place of your exam and plan your journey, allowing plenty of time to make sure you're there on time.

○ **What do I need to take?** Make sure you have everything you need for the exam including pens, highlighters and water.

○ **Relax!** Your revision is complete. Give yourself some time to relax and get an early night to make sure you're ready for the exam tomorrow.

MY FUNCTIONAL SKILLS EXAMS

Calculator paper

Date:

Time:

Location:

Non-calculator paper

Date:

Time:

Location:

Assessment breakdown

Structure

There are two sections to the assessment:

- Section A: a short non-calculator section worth 25 per cent of your total marks.
- Section B: a longer calculator section worth 75 per cent of your total marks.
- The time available to complete each section will vary depending on your exam board; you should check this information carefully.
- Most exam boards offer the assessment as a paper-based or an onscreen assessment.

Question types

- There is a mix of short (one mark only) questions and longer (2–6 mark) questions.
- Workings are not required for questions worth just one mark, as there are no method marks awarded (the mark is awarded for just the correct answer).
- Workings are important for all questions worth more than 1 mark.
- You should expect to see questions from each learning objective covered in this book on the exam paper.

- Some questions (especially longer 'wordier' questions) will require skills outlined in more than one objective.

Answering exam questions

- Some questions in your Functional Skills exam may contain a lot of information (for example, questions involve large numbers, fractions and numbers with decimal points) and one of the most important skills required is the ability to read each question and understand what the question is asking.
- This skill comes with practice, experience and increased confidence. Use the exam-style questions in this book to help you with this.
- It is important to write out clear workings in a logical order in your answers particularly for longer questions. As well as being helpful to you, clear workings can gain method marks. This means even if you do not give a fully correct answer, you may still get some marks for your working.
- It is important to check your answer includes the correct units, for example £, m, cm^2, g, kg, miles and so on.

1 Using numbers and the number system

DIAGNOSTIC QUESTIONS

 Non-calculator questions

1. a Convert $9\frac{2}{7}$ to an improper fraction.

   b Convert $\frac{139}{12}$ to a mixed number.

   c Calculate $2\frac{4}{5} + 2\frac{2}{3}$

   d Calculate $2\frac{1}{6} - 1\frac{1}{4}$

2. Place the following decimals in order from smallest to largest:

   0.92   0.928   −0.982   0.98   −0.908

3. What fraction of 14 is 6? Give your answer in its simplest form.

4. Write the following number in digits:

   one million, two hundred and fourteen thousand, six hundred and eight.

5. Show the amount of the circle shaded as:

   a a fraction

   b a percentage

   c a decimal.

6. Noel sees the following recipe to make twenty-four biscuits:

   100 g unsalted butter   75 g caster sugar
   1 free range egg   1 lemon
   200 g plain flour   50 g currants
   30 mL milk

He wants to make 60 biscuits. Calculate:

   a the amount of currants (in grams)

   b the amount of milk (in mL)

   c the amount of plain flour (in kg) he needs.

The biscuits are 6 cm in diameter. He places them on baking trays that measure 36 cm by 27 cm.

   d Calculate how many baking trays he will need.

7. a Calculate 49×31

   b Check your answer using estimation.

   c Calculate $3 \times 4 \div 2^2$

 Calculator questions

8. Calculate:

   a 0.55×0.708

   b $0.816 \div 0.32$

9. A window repair company charges £45 an hour for their services plus a call out fee of £35. Calculate how much the company would charge for $3\frac{1}{2}$ hours work.

10. Calculate 23% of £97.

11. The number of book sales in a shop increases from 87 on day 1 to 123 on day 2. Calculate the percentage increase in book sales from day 1 to day 2. Give your answer to one decimal place.

1.1 Read, write, order and compare positive and negative numbers of any size

Reading and writing numbers

For numbers greater than a thousand, a comma (or space) represents the word 'thousand' and separates the thousands from the next three digits.

For example: 18,706 (or 18 706) = eighteen thousand, seven hundred and six.

For numbers greater than a million, a comma (or space) represents the word 'million', followed by three digits and another comma to represent 'thousand', and another three digits.

For example: 5,083,206 = five million, eighty-three thousand, two hundred and six.

> **COMMON MISTAKE**
>
> Mistakes can happen when reading or writing large numbers. A part may be left out, or the digits may be separated too much. Be sure to read and write out each number carefully.

Ordering and comparing positive numbers

- The more digits a positive number has, the larger its size.
  For example: 648,560 is larger than 89,785
- If two positive numbers have the same number of digits, the number with the bigger first digit is the larger number. If the first digits are the same, the second digit determines which is the larger number.
  For example: **4**,028,574 is larger than **3**,859,620
              64,512,786 is larger than 63,890,903

Ordering and comparing negative numbers

- The fewer digits a negative number has, the larger its size.
  For example: −94,468 is larger than −112,386
- If two negative numbers have the same number of digits, then the number with the smaller first digit is the larger number. If the first digits are the same, the second digit will determine which is the larger number.
  For example: −**6**,935 is larger than −**8**,620
              −4**3**7,231 is larger than −4**5**2,847

WORKED EXAMPLE

Write the following numbers in numerical order from smallest to largest:

(97,640) (−31,560) (98,430) (−201,350) (107,650) (−31,480)

ANSWER

The negative number with the most digits is the smallest. The other two negative numbers start with the same two digits, so the number with the largest third digit is the next smallest.

Place the positive numbers together and align them. The number with the most digits is the largest. The other two positive numbers start with the same digit, so the number with the larger second digit is the next largest number.

From smallest to largest:

−201,350   −31,560   −31,480   97,640   98,430   107,650

CHECK YOUR UNDERSTANDING

1   Write 2,304,032 in words.
2   Write ninety-one million, eight hundred and forty-five thousand and forty nine as a number.
3   Write the following numbers in numerical order from smallest to largest:

(−84,084) (834,127) (−82,609) (98,679) (−108,202) (89,980)

1.2 Carry out calculations with numbers up to one million including strategies to check answers including estimation and approximation

Every day, people carry out calculations involving addition, subtraction, multiplication and division. Many of the questions in Functional Skills tests are based on real-life situations.

EXAM TIP

It is important when carrying out calculations (addition, subtraction, multiplication or division) that digits are aligned correctly i.e. tens with tens, hundreds with hundreds etc.

Checking the answer

Estimation and approximation are used a lot to check calculations. An estimate is a rough, but meaningful, answer, found quickly, without using a calculator.

Estimation: a rough calculation to find a value.

Approximation (rounding): finding a value that is close to the correct answer but not exactly equal to it.

COMMON MISTAKE

A common mistake is not reading the term estimation or approximation in a question, and instead, carrying out the exact calculation.

WORKED EXAMPLE

A climate change conference attracts 22,274 delegates, 14,124 observers and 3,886 media representatives. Calculate how many people attended the conference.

ANSWER

First, add the three values together to calculate the total number of people.

```
   22,274
   14,124
 +  3,886
 ─────────
   40,284
    1 1  1 1
```

To check the calculation, subtract one of the three numbers from the total and check it against the sum of the other two numbers. For example:

```
 ³4¹0̷,284        14,124
 – 2 2,274    +   3,886
 ─────────       ───────
   1 8,010        18,010
                   1 1 1
```

We can also check the above calculation by approximation. We can approximate by rounding each number to the nearest 1,000.

22,274	is approximately	22,000
14,124	is approximately	14,000
3,886	is approximately	4,000

When rounding to the nearest 1,000, check the hundreds column (indicated above in red). If the number of hundreds is 5, 6, 7, 8 or 9, round up the number in the 'thousands' column ('3' becomes '4' above). If the number of hundreds is 4, 3, 2, 1 or 0, then the number in the 'thousands' column stays the same ('2' stays as '2' and '4' stays as '4' above).

So, 22,000 + 14,000 + 4,000 = **40,000**

40,000 is close to 40,284 so the estimation suggests the answer is correct.

WORKED EXAMPLE

A company sells 23,486 tickets for a pop festival. If the tickets cost £96 each, then calculate the amount the company receives from ticket sales.

ANSWER

$$
\begin{array}{r}
23,486 \\
\times \quad 96 \\
\hline
140,916 \\
2,113,740 \\
\hline
2,254,656 = \textbf{£2,254,656}
\end{array}
$$

Use estimation to check the answer.

£23,486 rounded to the nearest thousand = £23,000
and £96 rounded to the nearest ten = £100

23,000 × 100 = 2,300,000

£2,300,000 is close to £2,254,656 so the estimate supports the answer.

EXAM TIP

Remember, the 9 in the 96 represents 90, so the second line of the calculation will start with a zero, as its place value is ten times that of the 6.

CHECK YOUR UNDERSTANDING

1   A further education college has 16,534 part-time students and 4,087 full-time students.
    How many students does it have in total? Show by a check of your answer.

2   A couple together take home £3,558 per month. They pay £1,450 in rent, £328 in bills and £155 in insurance costs. They save a fifth of the money left for a deposit for a house.
    Calculate how much they save per month. Show a check of your answer.

3   A charity sells tickets for a concert. It sells 419 tickets (standing only) for £37 each and 192 tickets for £72 each (for seats).
    Calculate how much money the charity raises.

1.3 Evaluate expressions and make substitutions in given formulae in words and symbols

Evaluating expressions

An **expression** in maths is a statement that includes at least two terms, containing numbers or variables (e.g. a, b, x, y, etc.) or both, separated by an operator (+, −, × or ÷) between them. Expressions do not have an equals sign (=).

For example:

- $6 - b$
- $y \div 3$
- $2x$ (2 multiplied by x)
- pq (p multiplied by q)

To evaluate an expression, **substitute** (replace) the variables (e.g. b or y) with numbers.

Formulae

A **formula** shows the relationship between the variables. The symbols represent amounts that can be changed. For example, the formula for working out the area of a triangle is:

In words: half of the base of the triangle multiplied by its height.

In symbols: $\frac{1}{2} \times b \times h$ (or $\frac{1}{2}bh$)

If we know the base and height values (e.g., if $b = 4\,cm$ and $h = 8\,cm$), then we use substitution. The values replace the symbols or words to calculate the area:

$$\text{Area} = \frac{1}{2} \times 4\,cm \times 8\,cm = 16\,cm^2$$

The base and height (b and h) of different sized triangles will vary, but the formula will remain the same.

> **Expression**: a sentence with a minimum of two numbers or variables and at least one mathematical operation.
>
> **Formula**: a mathematical rule, stated in words or mathematical symbols, for working out a value or an amount.

> **MAKING LINKS**
>
> Calculating area is covered in Section 2.4, page 55.

WORKED EXAMPLE

a A charity shop sells jumpers for £12 and shirts for £7. One day, it sells 6 jumpers and 8 shirts. How much does it make selling jumpers and shirts that day?

ANSWER

First, write a formula in words.

Money made = (Number of jumpers sold × £12) + (Number of shirts sold × £7)

Then write the word formula in symbols. Use J to represent the number of jumpers sold and S for the number of shirts sold.

So, money made = $12J + 7S$

Use your formula to calculate the amount the shop makes from the sales of jumpers and shirts by substituting the variables with the actual number of shirts and jumpers sold.

Money made = (6 × £12) + (8 × £7) = £72 + £56 = **£128**

> **EXAM TIP**
>
> As the two expressions do not depend on each other for their values, we can use brackets to separate them.

> **EXAM TIP**
>
> $12J$ means $12 \times J$, but we write it as $12J$ to avoid the confusion of having the × and J together.

b The next day, the shop sells 5 jumpers and 6 shirts. How much does it make on that day from the sale of jumpers and shirts?

ANSWER

We can substitute the numbers from part **b** into the formula we wrote in part **a** to calculate the money made.

Money made = $(5 \times £12) + (6 \times £7) = £60 + £42 =$ **£102**

WORKED EXAMPLE

a A plumber charges £40 an hour for her services plus a £25 call-out fee. Calculate the cost of hiring the plumber for $4\frac{1}{2}$ hours work.

ANSWER

First, write out the formula in words:

Cost = (number of hours $\times$ £40) + £25

Then write the formula in symbols. The number of hours worked can be represented by H.

Cost = $40H + 25$

Cost = $(4\frac{1}{2} \times 40) + 25 = 180 + 25 =$ **£205**

b Calculate the cost of hiring the same plumber for 6 hours of work.

ANSWER

The formula from part **a** can be used to work out the cost of any number of hours worked. Substitute the values in part **b** into the formula.

Cost = $(6 \times 40) + 25 = 240 + 25 =$ **£265**

CHECK YOUR UNDERSTANDING

1 A warehouse employee can pack 28 boxes in an hour. Calculate how many boxes he can pack in 4 hours 15 mins.

2 A tailor makes 8 memory cushions and 3 memory pillows for a family. He charges £12 for the cushions and £9 for the pillows. Calculate the total cost of the cushions and pillows.

3 A student records the temperature on a thermometer as 77° Fahrenheit (°F).
Calculate the temperature in degrees Celsius (°C). Use the conversion formula $C = (F - 32) \times \frac{5}{9}$

1.4 Identify and know the equivalence between fractions, decimals and percentages

Fractions, decimals and percentages are different ways of representing a proportion of the same amount. They all mean 'part of a whole'.

- Fractions have a **numerator** and a **denominator**. In this circle, there are 8 equal parts and 5 are shaded. So, the fraction of the circle shaded is $\frac{5}{8}$ (five eighths).

- Decimals are a way of writing numbers that are not whole, for example 0.25. Decimal numbers can be recognised as they have a decimal point.

- Percentages are numbers that are expressed as parts of 100. Percent means 'number of parts per hundred'. The symbol used for percent is %. For example, 27% means 27 parts per (out of a) hundred.

> **Numerator:** the top number in a fraction, shows how many of the equal parts there are.
>
> **Denominator:** the bottom number in a fraction, how many equal parts the whole has been divided into.
>
> **Equivalence:** two or more numbers or quantities that are the same.

Equivalence

There is **equivalence** between fractions, decimals and percentages.

For example, $\frac{3}{10} = 0.3 = 30\%$

It is useful to remember some common (everyday) equivalences, for example, a half, a quarter, three quarters, a fifth, a third.

$\frac{1}{2} = 50\% = 0.5$ $\frac{1}{4} = 25\% = 0.25$ $\frac{3}{4} = 75\% = 0.75$ $\frac{1}{5} = 20\% = 0.2$ $\frac{1}{3} = 33\% = 0.3\dot{3}$

However, for less common fractions, percentages and decimals, methods are needed to convert between them.

Converting a fraction to a decimal or percentage
To convert from a fraction to a decimal, you can divide the numerator by the denominator:

$\frac{1}{8}$ is 1 divided by 8

$$8\overline{)1.0^20^40} = \mathbf{0.125}$$

To convert from a fraction to a percentage, you multiply by 100 (then add %).

> **EXAM TIP**
>
> To **simplify** the fraction (reduce it to its simplest form), do the same operation (× or ÷) to the numerator and denominator.

$\frac{3}{8} \times 100 = \frac{300}{8} \begin{array}{c} \div 4 \\ \div 4 \end{array} = \frac{75}{2} = 37.5 = \mathbf{37.5\%}$

$\frac{2}{3} \times 100 = \frac{200}{3} = \mathbf{66.\dot{6}}$ or **66.7% to 1 decimal place**

Converting a decimal to a percentage or a fraction
To convert from a decimal to a percentage, you multiply by 100 (then add the % sign to the answer).

So, $0.125 \times 100 = \mathbf{12.5\%}$

$0.286 \times 100 = \mathbf{28.6\%}$

To convert from a decimal to a fraction, you can multiply by 100 (then add the % to form a percentage), then convert to a fraction (out of a hundred) and simplify:

$$0.16 \times 100 = 16\% = \frac{16}{100} = \frac{4}{25}$$

$$0.875 \times 100 = 87.5\% = \frac{87.5}{100} \begin{array}{c} \times 2 \\ \times 2 \end{array} = \frac{\cancel{175}^{7}}{\cancel{200}^{8}} = \frac{7}{8}$$

Converting a percentage to a decimal or a fraction

To convert from a percentage to a decimal, you divide by 100:

$$23\% = \frac{23}{100} = \mathbf{0.23} \qquad 62.5\% = \frac{62.5}{100} = \mathbf{0.625} \qquad 8\% = \frac{8}{100} = \mathbf{0.08}$$

To convert from a percentage to a fraction, divide by 100, then simplify (if you can):

$$24\% = \frac{24}{100} \begin{array}{c} \div 4 \\ \div 4 \end{array} = \frac{\mathbf{6}}{\mathbf{25}} \qquad 9\% = \frac{\mathbf{9}}{\mathbf{100}} \qquad 62.5\% = \frac{62.5}{100} \begin{array}{c} \times 2 \\ \times 2 \end{array} = \frac{\mathbf{5}}{\mathbf{8}}$$

EXAM TIP

It is useful to remember the eighths as percentages and decimals. They can be calculated by multiplying 12.5% and 0.125 by 3, 5 and 7 (e.g., 12.5% × 3 = 37.5% and 0.125 × 5 = 0.625 etc.).

$\frac{1}{8} = 12.5\% = 0.125$ $\frac{3}{8} = 37.5\% = 0.375$ $\frac{5}{8} = 62.5\% = 0.625$ $\frac{7}{8} = 87.5\% = 0.875$

WORKED EXAMPLE

Look at the following diagram and calculate how much of the circle is shaded. Give your answer as:

    a   a fraction

    b   a percentage (to one decimal place)

    c   a decimal (to three decimal places).

ANSWER

    a   One part in six is shaded, so the fraction is $\frac{1}{6}$.

    b $\frac{1}{6} \times 100\% = \frac{100}{6} = \frac{50}{3}$

$$\begin{array}{r} 1\ 6.\ 6\ \dot{6} \\ 3\overline{)\ 5^{2}0.^{2}0^{2}0} \end{array} = \mathbf{16.7\% \text{ (to 1 decimal place)}}$$

    c   Convert the percentage into a decimal:

$$16.7\% = \frac{16.7}{100} = \mathbf{0.167 \text{ (to 3 decimal places)}}$$

CHECK YOUR UNDERSTANDING

1 Calculate how much of the circle is shaded. Give your answer as:
   a   a fraction
   b   a decimal (to three decimal places)
   c   a percentage (to one decimal place).

2 Place the following in order from largest to smallest:

   $\dfrac{75}{100}$ 0.715   71.7% $\dfrac{14}{20}$ 0.72   72.5%

3 Mahipal is doing a 5,000-piece jigsaw. He has 760 pieces remaining.
   Calculate how much of the jigsaw he has already completed as:
   a   a fraction
   b   a decimal
   c   a percentage.

1.5 Work out percentages of amounts and express one amount as a percentage of another

REVISED ○

Calculating percentages of amounts

There are different ways of working out percentages of amounts.

 Method 1

The percentage is first converted to a fraction out of a hundred, and then multiplied by the amount.

WORKED EXAMPLE

Calculate 75% of £54.

ANSWER

75% as a fraction is $\frac{3}{4}$

$\frac{3}{4} \times 54 = \frac{162}{4}$

$$4\overline{)162.^20}\ \ \ \ 40.5 = \textbf{£40.50}$$

EXAM TIP

75% of 54 is equal to 54% of 75 since in both calculations, the numerators are the same and the denominator is the same. Look out for other similar examples!

WORKED EXAMPLE

Calculate 20% of £35.50

ANSWER

20% as a fraction is $\frac{20}{100}$

Simplify:

$\frac{20}{100} = \frac{2\cancel{0}}{10\cancel{0}} = \frac{2}{10}$

Multiply the simplified fraction by £35.50:

$\frac{2}{10} \times 35.50 = \frac{71}{10} = \textbf{£7.10}$

COMMON MISTAKES

A common mistake would be cancelling the 0 in the £35.50 with the 0 in the denominator or leaving the answer as 7.1 instead of £7.10.

 Method 2

The percentage of an amount can be changed to a fraction out of a hundred, then simplified.

WORKED EXAMPLE

Calculate 12.5% of £56.

ANSWER

Change 12.5% into a fraction over 100: $\frac{12.5}{100}$

Simplify:

$\frac{12.5}{100} = \frac{25}{200} = \frac{25^1}{200^8} = \frac{1}{8}$

Multiply the simplified fraction by £56:

$\frac{1}{\cancel{8}^1} \times \cancel{56}^7 = \frac{7}{1} = \textbf{£7}$

EXAM TIP

With fractions, you can do the same to the numerator and denominator, without changing the value of the fraction. This is called **simplifying** the fraction. In the example here, both the numerator and the denominator in $\frac{12.5}{100}$ are multiplied by 2.

Method 3

The percentage of an amount can be converted to a decimal and calculated using a calculator.

WORKED EXAMPLE

Calculate 9% of £18.

ANSWER

9% as a decimal is 0.09.

Multiply 0.09 by 18: $0.09 \times £18 = \textbf{£1.62}$

Expressing one amount as a percentage of another

When expressing one amount as a percentage of another, form a fraction first, (simplify if necessary), then multiply by 100%. For example:

Express 7 as a percentage of 20

$$\frac{7}{20^{1}} \times \cancel{100}^{5}\% = \textbf{35\%}$$

What percentage of 12.5 is 7?

$$\frac{7 \times 2}{12.5 \times 2} = \frac{14}{25^{1}} \times \cancel{100}^{4}\% = \textbf{56\%}$$

WORKED EXAMPLE

Dariusz and his family drive from London to Newcastle. If their journey time is five hours, what percentage of the time of their journey have they completed after two hours and fifteen minutes?

ANSWER

First, express two hours and fifteen minutes in hours:

$$2 \text{ hours } 15 \text{ minutes} = 2\frac{1}{4} \text{ hours} = 2.25 \text{ hours}$$

Then, to find what percentage of the time 2.25 hours is, form a fraction (out of the journey time 5 hours), multiply by 100 and add the percentage sign (%).

$$\frac{2.25}{5} \times 100 = \frac{225}{5} = \textbf{45\%}$$

CHECK YOUR UNDERSTANDING

 1 Calculate:

a 20% of £84

b 84% of £20

c 62.5% of 160L

d 17.5% of £240.

 2 A teacher records the ages of a class of 20 adults in a frequency table. What percentage of her students are aged 40 or above?

Age (a) in years	Frequency
Under 20	2
20 to 29	7
30 to 39	4
40 to 50	3
50+	4

 3 In the following pie chart, the green shaded area represents 35% of the circle. Calculate the angle of the shaded area.

1.6 Calculate percentage change (any size increase and decrease), and original value after percentage change

Calculating percentage change

To work out a percentage change between two numbers (which can be an increase or decrease), first work out the difference between the two numbers you are comparing.

Then, form a fraction by dividing the difference by the original number, multiply the answer by 100 and add % to convert the fraction to a percentage.

The following formula can be used:

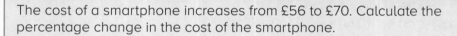

$$\text{Percentage change} = \frac{\text{actual change}}{\text{original amount}} \times 100\%$$

> **Percentage change:** the difference (or change) between two amounts, divided by the original amount, then multiplied by 100%.

WORKED EXAMPLE

The cost of a smartphone increases from £56 to £70. Calculate the percentage change in the cost of the smartphone.

ANSWER

First, find the actual change: £70 − £56 = £14

Then form a fraction using the percentage change formula above, multiply it by 100 and add the % sign.

$$\frac{14}{56} \times 100 = \mathbf{25\%}$$

> **EXAM TIP**
>
> If you can, simplify the fraction first. If you know what the fraction is as a percentage, then state it. In this example:
>
> $$\frac{14}{56} = \frac{1}{4} = 25\%$$

WORKED EXAMPLE

The cost of a suit is reduced in a sale from £165 to £119.99. Ahmed thinks that the suit has been reduced by more than 30%. Is Ahmed correct?

ANSWER

First, calculate the actual change: £165 − £119.99 = £45.01

Then, form a fraction and multiply by 100 (adding %) to calculate the percentage change (decrease).

$$\frac{45.01}{165} \times 100 = 27.3\% \text{ to 1 decimal place}$$

27.3% is less than 30% so Ahmed is not correct.

Calculating the original value after percentage change

The original value of an item, after it has increased or decreased (following a percentage change) to its current value, can be found by first calculating 1% of its current value, then multiplying by 100%.

To find 1% of the current value, divide the current value by the percentage it is of the original value.

For example, if an item bought for £60 includes VAT of 20%, then the price is 120% of the original value.

$$1\% \text{ of } 60 = \frac{60}{120} = \frac{6}{12} = \frac{1}{2}$$

$$\frac{1}{2} \times 100 = \textbf{£50}$$

WORKED EXAMPLE

Example exam-style question

A suit is on sale for £78 after it has been reduced by 20%. Calculate the original price.

> **ANSWER**
>
> The suit has been reduced from its original value of 100% by 20%. So, the current value is 80% of the original value.
>
> To calculate the original value, find 1% of the current value of the item by dividing the sale cost (£78) by 80 (the value after discount). Then multiply the result by 100.
>
> $$\frac{78}{80} \times 100 = \textbf{£97.50}$$

COMMON MISTAKE

A common mistake, when calculating the original value, is to divide the current value by 100, instead of finding 1%.

WORKED EXAMPLE

Example exam-style question

In an auction, a gold ring is sold for £650, a 25% increase on the price it was originally bought for. How much was the gold ring originally bought for?

> **ANSWER**
>
> If the gold ring increased in value by 25%, it is now worth 125% of its original value.
>
> To find the ring's original value, calculate 1% of the value of the item (divide the sale cost by 125), then multiply the result by 100.
>
> $$\frac{650}{125} \times 100 = \textbf{£520}$$

CHECK YOUR UNDERSTANDING

 1   A wardrobe is reduced in price in a sale from £120 to £78. Calculate the percentage decrease.

 2   A vintage car is sold for 35% more than it was originally bought for. It was sold for £10,800. Calculate how much it was originally bought for.

3   A man uses a line graph to record the sales of two new books for
     the first five days following their release.

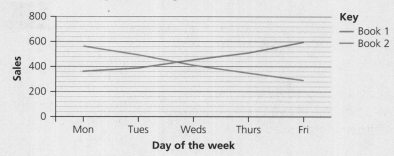

Calculate:

a   The percentage increase in sales of book 1 over the 5 days
     (give your answer to one decimal place).

b   The percentage decrease in sales of book 2 over the 5 days.

1.7 Order, add, subtract and compare amounts or quantities using proper and improper fractions and mixed numbers

Remember from Level 1 that there are proper fractions (e.g. $\frac{1}{2}$), improper fractions (e.g. $\frac{8}{3}$) and mixed numbers (e.g. $5\frac{1}{3}$).

To order, add, subtract and compare amounts using proper fractions, improper fractions and mixed numbers, we sometimes have to convert mixed numbers to improper fractions or improper fractions to mixed numbers.

Ordering and comparing proper and improper fractions and mixed numbers

WORKED EXAMPLE

Place the following in order, from smallest to largest:

$$1\frac{4}{5} \qquad \frac{7}{3} \qquad \frac{9}{10} \qquad 1\frac{3}{4} \qquad 2\frac{2}{3}$$

ANSWER

Here, we must compare the numbers so that we can order them. $\frac{9}{10}$ is the only proper fraction and it will be the smallest number as it is the only number less than one.

To compare the rest of the numbers, convert them into the same format. Here, convert the improper fraction into a mixed number.

$$\frac{7}{3} = 2\frac{1}{3}$$

So as mixed numbers the other items are: $1\frac{4}{5}$, $2\frac{1}{3}$, $1\frac{3}{4}$, $2\frac{2}{3}$

To compare $1\frac{4}{5}$ and $1\frac{3}{4}$, compare the fraction part of each mixed number (they have the same integer). To compare $\frac{4}{5}$ and $\frac{3}{4}$, find the lowest common denominator. List the multiples of each fraction's denominator until you find the first number that is on both lists:

5: 5, 10, 15, **20**

4: 4, 8, 12, 16, **20**

Find the equivalent fractions for $\frac{4}{3}$ and $\frac{3}{4}$ by multiplying the numerators and denominators by the same number to get 20 as the denominator:

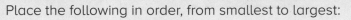

$$\frac{4}{5} = \frac{16}{20} \quad \text{and} \quad \frac{3}{4} = \frac{15}{20}$$

$\frac{15}{20}$ is less than $\frac{16}{20}$ so $1\frac{3}{4}$ is smaller than $1\frac{4}{5}$.

Comparing $2\frac{1}{3}$ and $2\frac{2}{3}$, $2\frac{2}{3}$ is a larger mixed number than $2\frac{1}{3}$.

Therefore, the order is: $\frac{9}{10}$, $1\frac{3}{4}$, $1\frac{4}{5}$, $\frac{7}{3}$, $2\frac{2}{3}$.

Proper fraction: a fraction that is less than one, with the numerator less than the denominator.

Improper fraction: a fraction in which the numerator is greater than the denominator.

Mixed number: a number consisting of an integer and a proper fraction.

MAKING LINKS

Converting, ordering and comparing proper fractions, improper fractions and mixed numbers is covered in detail in Level 1, Section 1.8.

EXAM TIP

If the larger denominator (5) is not a multiple of the smaller denominator (4), then the lowest common denominator can also be found by multiplying the two numbers together: $4 \times 5 = 20$

Lowest common denominator: the smallest number that can be divided exactly by all the denominators in a group of two or more fractions.

Multiple: a number you get when you multiply a given number by an integer. For example, multiples of 6 are 12, 18, 24, 30 etc.

Adding and subtracting proper fractions

WORKED EXAMPLE

Calculate $\frac{1}{4} + \frac{2}{7}$

ANSWER

When adding or subtracting fractions, find the lowest common denominator.

The larger denominator (7) is not a multiple of the smaller denominator (4). So find the lowest common denominator by multiplying the denominators of $\frac{1}{4}$ and $\frac{2}{7}$.

$4 \times 7 = 28$

The numerators are multiplied by the same number:

$$\frac{1}{4} = \frac{7}{28} \quad \text{and} \quad \frac{2}{7} = \frac{8}{28}$$

($\times 7$ top and bottom; $\times 4$ top and bottom)

With the same common denominator, the two fractions can be added.

$$\frac{7}{28} + \frac{8}{28} = \frac{7+8}{28} = \frac{15}{28}$$

EXAM TIP

Remember (from Section 1.5), with fractions, we can do the same to the numerator and denominator, without changing the value of the fraction.

WORKED EXAMPLE

Calculate: $\frac{7}{8} - \frac{1}{4}$

ANSWER

Here, the larger denominator (8) is a multiple of the smaller denominator (4). The lowest common denominator is therefore 8. So $\frac{1}{4}$ will be changed to have the same denominator as $\frac{7}{8}$.

The denominator of $\frac{1}{4}$ is divided into the lowest common denominator. The numerator is multiplied by the result.

$$\frac{1}{4} = \frac{2}{8}$$

($\times 2$ top and bottom)

With the same common denominator, the two fractions can be subtracted.

$$\frac{7}{8} - \frac{2}{8} = \frac{7-2}{8} = \frac{5}{8}$$

EXAM TIP

Sometimes, if two proper fractions are added, the result is an improper fraction (which is larger than 1). This can then be converted to a mixed number.

Adding and subtracting mixed numbers and improper fractions

Calculate $3\frac{1}{6}+4\frac{3}{7}$. Give your answer as a mixed number.

ANSWER

To add two mixed numbers together, first add the integers (whole numbers).

Then add the proper fractions separately (after converting the fractions to have the same denominator).

Find the lowest common denominator (in this example $6 \times 7 = 42$).

$$3\frac{1}{6}+4\frac{3}{7}=7+\frac{1}{6}+\frac{3}{7}$$

$$\frac{1}{6}+\frac{3}{7}=\frac{7+18}{42}=\frac{25}{42}$$

So

$$3\frac{1}{6}+4\frac{3}{7}=\mathbf{7\frac{25}{42}}$$

Calculate $5\frac{2}{3}-2\frac{3}{4}$. Give your answer as a mixed number.

ANSWER

To subtract mixed numbers, they can first be converted to improper fractions:

$$5\frac{2}{3}=\frac{17}{3} \quad \text{and} \quad 2\frac{3}{4}=\frac{11}{4}$$

Then find the lowest common denominator for the two improper fractions and subtract them. The lowest common denominator here is 12.

$$\frac{17}{3}-\frac{11}{4}=\frac{68-33}{12}=\frac{35}{12}$$

After the answer has been calculated as an improper fraction, it can be converted back to a mixed number.

$$\frac{35}{12}=\mathbf{2\frac{11}{12}}$$

WORKED EXAMPLE

Calculate $\frac{47}{6}+\frac{74}{9}$.

ANSWER

To add two improper fractions together, first convert them to mixed numbers, then add the integers and the proper fractions separately, as in a previous example.

$$\frac{47}{6}+\frac{74}{9}=7\frac{5}{6}+8\frac{2}{9}=15+\frac{5}{6}+\frac{2}{9}$$

In this example, the lowest common denominator can be found by listing the multiples of 6 and 9 and finding the first number that is on both lists, which is 18.

$$\frac{5}{6}+\frac{2}{9}=\frac{15+4}{18}=\frac{19}{18}=1\frac{1}{18}$$

So

$$15+1\frac{1}{18}=\mathbf{16\frac{1}{18}}$$

CHECK YOUR UNDERSTANDING

1 Place the following in order from largest to smallest:

$1\frac{1}{9}$ $\frac{20}{21}$ $\frac{13}{14}$ $\frac{11}{10}$ $1\frac{1}{8}$

2 Calculate:

a $\frac{4}{5}+1\frac{2}{3}$

b $\frac{4}{5}-\frac{1}{4}$

3 Calculate:

a $6\frac{2}{3}+\frac{15}{4}$

b $7\frac{1}{5}-3\frac{1}{2}$

Give your answers as mixed numbers.

1.8 Express one number as a fraction of another

When expressing one number as a fraction of another, a proper fraction is formed by placing the smaller number (numerator) over the larger number (denominator). Then the fraction is simplified if necessary.

WORKED EXAMPLE

Express 12 as a fraction of 60.

ANSWER

Here, 12 becomes the numerator over the denominator, 60. The fraction formed $\left(\frac{12}{60}\right)$ can then be simplified by dividing the numerator and denominator by 12.

$$\frac{12}{60} \begin{array}{c} \div 12 \\ \div 12 \end{array} = \frac{\cancel{12}^{1}}{\cancel{60}^{5}} = \frac{1}{5}$$

WORKED EXAMPLE

What fraction of £22.50 is £7?

ANSWER

Here, £7 becomes the numerator over the denominator £22.50. The fraction formed $\left(\frac{7}{22.50}\right)$ can then be simplified by multiplying the numerator and denominator by 2, to remove the decimal point from the denominator and form a proper fraction.

$$\frac{7}{22.5} \begin{array}{c} \times 2 \\ \times 2 \end{array} = \frac{14}{45}$$

COMMON MISTAKE

For one number to be a fraction of (or a part of) another, the smaller number must be the numerator and the larger number must be the denominator.

WORKED EXAMPLE

Zahra needs to travel 120 miles to her destination. After 102 miles, what fraction of her journey is remaining?

ANSWER

In this example, the amount of her remaining journey is the numerator, while the whole journey is the denominator.

The amount of journey remaining = 120 − 102 = 18 miles

So, fraction of journey remaining $= \dfrac{18}{120} \begin{array}{c} \div 2 \\ \div 2 \end{array} = \dfrac{\cancel{18}^{9}}{\cancel{120}^{60}}$

$= \dfrac{9}{60} \begin{array}{c} \div 3 \\ \div 3 \end{array} = \dfrac{\cancel{9}^{3}}{\cancel{60}^{20}} = \dfrac{3}{20}$

Or $\dfrac{18}{120} \begin{array}{c} \div 6 \\ \div 6 \end{array} = \dfrac{\cancel{18}^{3}}{\cancel{120}^{20}} = \dfrac{3}{20}$

COMMON MISTAKES

Common mistakes here include using the incorrect number for the numerator and/or forgetting to simplify the fraction.

WORKED EXAMPLE

On a plane carrying 320 passengers, 40 are travelling first class. If the rest are travelling economy, calculate the fraction of passengers travelling economy.

ANSWER

$320 - 40 = 280$ passengers travelling economy out of a total of 320.

$$\frac{280}{320} = \frac{28}{32} \begin{array}{c} \div 4 \\ \div 4 \end{array} = \frac{7}{8}$$

EXAM TIP

Remember, with fractions, you can do the same to the numerator and denominator to form an equivalent fraction i.e. without changing the value of the fraction; in this example, dividing both by 10 and then by 4.

CHECK YOUR UNDERSTANDING

1 Out of a class of forty-two students, fourteen are aged eighteen or above. What fraction of students in the class are under eighteen?

2 The angle within the blue shaded area of this pie chart is 99°. Calculate the fraction of the circle that is shaded lilac.

3 Daljit pays £390 a month for her car insurance and £7.50 a week for breakdown cover. What fraction of the total annual cost of the two payments does she pay on her breakdown cover?

1.9 Order, approximate and compare decimals

REVISED

Ordering and comparing decimals

- To order decimals in terms of their size, align the digits correctly.
- The size of the first digit determines which the larger number is. For example, 0.034 is larger than 0.028.
- If the first digits are the same, the size of the second digit determines which is the larger number, for example, 0.250 is larger than 0.239, and so on.
- With negative decimals, the **smaller** the first digit after the decimal point, the **larger** is the decimal number. For example, −0.5 is larger than −0.8.
- If the first digit after the decimal point is the same in two negative decimal numbers, then the **smaller** the second digit after the decimal point, the **larger** is the decimal number. For example, −0.72 is larger than −0.76 and so on.

MAKING LINKS

Ordering and comparing decimals to three decimal places is covered in Level 1, Section 1.10.

EXAM TIP

Zeros can be placed at the end of a decimal number. They have no value but can help when comparing the sizes of decimal numbers.

WORKED EXAMPLE

Place the following decimals in numerical order, largest to smallest:

−0.426   −0.406   −0.416   −0.146   −0.10

ANSWER

This question is asking for the decimals to be placed in *descending* order, from largest to smallest.

Align the numbers on the decimal places. Then look at which digits are bigger.

    −0.426
    −0.406
    −0.416
    −0.146
    −0.160

So, the order is:

−0.146   −0.160   −0.406   −0.416   −0.426

Approximating decimals

Approximating is choosing a number that is close enough to a specific number. This process is also known as rounding.

60 ÷ 7 on a calculator equals 8.5714285714. It is unlikely we need an answer this accurate, so we approximate the decimal.

To write it to the nearest whole number, look at the first digit after the decimal point (in the tenths column):

- If this number is 5 or above (5, 6, 7, 8 or 9), round the digit in the units column up from 8 to 9.

- If the number is 4 or under (1, 2, 3 or 4), then the digit in the units column stays the same.

So, 8.5714285714 to the nearest whole number is **9**.

Writing numbers to decimal places

You may be asked to give an answer to X decimal place(s). This means having a certain number of digits after the decimal point.

WORKED EXAMPLE

Write the decimal 8.6714285714 to 3 decimal places.

> **ANSWER**
>
> This answer needs three digits after the decimal point. As this is in the thousandths column, you can also say 'to the nearest thousandth'.
>
> Look at the digit that is after the thousandths column. It is 4. This is below 5, so the digit in the thousandths column stays the same, 1.
>
> So, the above number to 3 decimal places (or to the nearest thousandth) = **8.671**

COMMON MISTAKE

It is a common mistake when asked to give a number to one decimal place (or two decimal places), for students to move the decimal one place (or two places), instead of rounding.

CHECK YOUR UNDERSTANDING

1   Place the following decimals in numerical order from smallest to largest:

    (0.635) (0.586) (−0.568) (−0.649) (−0.658) (−0.508)

2   A sprinter completes a 100 m race in 10.0946 seconds. State his time:
    a   to the nearest whole number
    b   to the nearest tenth of a second
    c   to the nearest hundredth of a second
    d   to the nearest thousandth of a second.

3   A family uses 2,653 units of electricity in 3 months. If the unit cost of electricity is 18.9p/kWh, using a calculator, work out the cost of their energy bill:
    a   to the nearest pound
    b   to the nearest 10p
    c   to the nearest penny.

EXAM TIP

As the bill will be in pounds, convert the unit cost (in pence) to pounds first by dividing it by a hundred. To the nearest 10p means to one decimal place followed by a zero and to the nearest penny means having 2 digits after the decimal point.

1.10 Add, subtract, multiply and divide decimals up to three decimal places

In Functional Skills Maths Level 2, we will be calculating with decimals that have up to three decimal places (three numbers after the decimal point).

Adding and subtracting decimals

When adding or subtracting decimals, you need to make sure that the decimal points and digits are aligned correctly (tenths with tenths and hundredths with hundredths etc.)

> **MAKING LINKS**
>
> Calculating with decimals up to two decimal places is covered in Level 1, Section 1.11.

WORKED EXAMPLE

Calculate 14.704 + 8.39

ANSWER

$$14.704 + 8.39 = \begin{array}{r} 14.704 \\ + 8.390 \\ \hline \mathbf{23.094} \\ \hline \end{array}$$

WORKED EXAMPLE

Calculate 25.2 − 9.568

ANSWER

$$25.2 - 9.568 = \begin{array}{r} 2\,5.\,2\,0\,0 \\ - 9.\,5\,6\,8 \\ \hline \mathbf{15.\,6\,3\,2} \\ \hline \end{array}$$

Multiplying decimals

When multiplying decimals, the decimal points can first be removed and the calculation done by long multiplication.

WORKED EXAMPLE

Calculate 0.627 × 0.354.

ANSWER

There are 6 digits after the decimal points, so there should then be 6 digits after the decimal point in the answer.

$$0.627 \times 0.354 \quad \begin{array}{r} 627 \\ \times\ 354 \\ \hline 2508 \\ 31350 \\ \underline{188100} \\ \underline{221958} \end{array}$$

So, answer = **0.221958**

> **EXAM TIP**
>
> When setting out calculations with decimals, make sure that the digits are correctly aligned with regards to their place value.

When multiplying by the 5 in the 354, start by placing a 0, because the place value of the 5 (hundredths) is ten times the place value of the 4 (thousandths).

Then, when multiplying by the 3 in the 354, start by placing 00 because the place value of the 3 (tenths) is a hundred times the place value of the 4 (thousandths).

EXAM TIP

In this calculation, it is more straightforward to write the longer decimal number above the shorter one.

Dividing decimals

When dividing decimals, you can first show the calculation as a fraction. Then consider how to convert it to remove the decimal point from the denominator.

EXAM TIP

Remember from Section 1.8, with fractions you do the same to the numerator and denominator to obtain an equivalent fraction without changing its value.

WORKED EXAMPLE

$3.81 \div 0.06$

> **ANSWER**
>
> $$3.81 \div 0.06 = \frac{3.81}{0.06} \begin{array}{c} \times 100 \\ \times 100 \end{array} = \frac{381}{6} = 6\overline{)38^2 1.^3 0}\ {}^{6\,3.\,5}$$

WORKED EXAMPLE

The following diagram shows the dimensions of a classroom. Calculate:

   a   the perimeter of the classroom (in m)

   b   the area of the classroom (in m²).

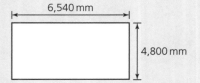

6,540 mm

4,800 mm

MAKING LINKS

How to calculate perimeter and area is explained in Section 2.4, page 55.

> **ANSWER**
>
> First, convert the dimensions to metres:
> 6,540 mm = 6.54 m and 4,800 mm = 4.8 m
>
> a Perimeter = 6.54
>   6.54
>   4.80
>   + 4.80
>   22.68 m
>   ²
>
> b Area = 6.54 m × 4.8 m   654 ³ ⁴
>   × 48 ¹ ²
>   5232
>   26160
>   31392
>   ¹
>
>   So, answer = **31.392 m²**

WORKED EXAMPLE

A bathroom wall is 2.2 m high and 3.5 m long. Calculate how many tiles measuring 25 cm by 25 cm are needed to cover the wall.

ANSWER

$25\,cm = 0.25\,m$

Number of tiles high $= \dfrac{2.2}{0.25} \begin{array}{c} \times\,4 \\ \times\,4 \end{array} = \dfrac{8.8}{1} = 8.8 = 9$ tiles

Number of tiles across $= \dfrac{3.5}{0.25} \begin{array}{c} \times\,4 \\ \times\,4 \end{array} = \dfrac{14}{1} = 14$ tiles

So, number of tiles $= 14 \times 9 = $ **126 tiles**

CHECK YOUR UNDERSTANDING

1 Calculate the range of the following lengths:

8.746 km	12.903 km	7.621 km	13.09 km	9.499 km

2 Calculate:
- a   2.789 + 1.046 + 0.33
- b   4.29 × 0.29
- c   5.92 ÷ 0.32.

3 The dimensions of a patio are 480 cm by 365 cm. A tin of varnish covers 1.5 m².

Calculate how many tins would be needed to varnish the patio.

MAKING LINKS

How to calculate the range is covered Section 3.3, page 88.

1.11 Understand and calculate using ratios, direct proportion and inverse proportion

Ratios

Ratios can be used to compare two or more amounts or quantities. They are written in a particular format. Ratios can be used to calculate individual and total amounts.

> **Ratio**: a way to compare (or show the relationship between) two or more quantities of the same kind.

For example, if there are 4 adults and 20 children in a classroom, the ratio of adults to children would be written as:

adults : children
   4 : 20
   1 : 5

Like fractions, ratios are normally expressed in their simplest form. To simplify a ratio, the same needs to be done to each amount. In the above example, the numbers on both sides (of the : sign) have been divided by 4.

WORKED EXAMPLE

Sarah, Mike and Andrew share £760 in the ratio of 4 : 3 : 1.

Calculate how much they each get.

ANSWER

It is good practice in ratio questions to write down what you are comparing and put the ratio underneath.

Sarah : Mike : Andrew
  4 : 3   : 1
  4 + 3 + 1 = 8 parts altogether

The total amount (£760) is divided by the number of parts it is shared by (8 parts) to find the amount for 1 part.

So, $760 \div 8 = 8\overline{)76^40}$ means £95 for 1 part.

Then, to find out how much each person gets, multiply 1 part by the ratio amounts:

Sarah: 4 × £95 = **£380**, Mike: 3 × £95 = **£285**, Andrew: 1 × £95 = **£95**

WORKED EXAMPLE

Sweets with 3 different colour wrappers are mixed in a tin. The ratio of red wrappers to green wrappers to yellow wrappers is 5 : 3 : 2. If there are 12 sweets with green wrappers in the box, calculate the number of sweets in the tin.

ANSWER

Here, the total number of sweets is not given. However, we can use the ratio and the amount of green wrappers to work out the other amounts and then the total.

red : green : yellow
 5 :   3   :   2

$12 \div 3 = 4$ for 1 part

Then, to find out the other amounts, multiply by the ratio amounts:

red = $5 \times 4 = $ **20** and yellow = $2 \times 4 = $ **8**

So, total = 20 + 12 + 8 = **40 sweets**

Proportion

Proportion is a mathematical comparison between two numbers.

Direct proportion

For two quantities to be in **direct proportion** to one another, the increase (or decrease) in one would cause the other to increase (or decrease) at the same rate.

Direct proportion can be used to calculate quantities when things are scaled up or scaled down. For example, if we know the cost of petrol in £ per litre, as the number of litres of petrol increases, the cost of the petrol increases in direct proportion.

> **Proportion:** the quantity, size or number of one thing or group as compared to the quantity, size or number of another.
>
> **Direct proportion:** when the increase (or decrease) in one quantity causes another quantity to increase (or decrease) in the same ratio.

WORKED EXAMPLE

A baker uses a recipe for 12 pancakes.
- 100 g plain flour
- 2 large eggs
- 300 mL milk
- 1 tbsp sunflower oil

  a Calculate the ingredients needed for 30 pancakes.
  b How much milk would be needed to make 7 pancakes?

ANSWER

a To make 30 pancakes, $\frac{30}{12} = 2\frac{1}{2}$ times more of each ingredient would be needed:

$100 \times 2\frac{1}{2} = $ **250 g** plain flour

$2 \times 2\frac{1}{2} = $ **5** large eggs

$300 \times 2\frac{1}{2} = $ **750 mL** milk

$1 \times 2\frac{1}{2} = \mathbf{2\frac{1}{2}}$ tbsp sunflower oil

b To find how much milk is needed to make 7 pancakes:

First, find the amount of milk needed for 1 pancake
= 300 mL ÷ 12 = 25 mL

Then, multiply by 7 to find the milk needed for 7 pancakes:
25 mL × 7 = **175 mL**

Inverse proportion

If the increase in a quantity causes another quantity to decrease at the same rate (or a decrease causes an increase) the quantities are in **inverse proportion** to one another. Inverse proportions can also be used to calculate amounts when things are scaled up or scaled down.

Inverse proportion: when the increase (or decrease) in one quantity causes another quantity to decrease (or increase) in the same ratio.

WORKED EXAMPLE

Three florists can make 60 bouquets of flowers in 4 hours. Calculate how long it would take eight florists to make 60 bouquets (assuming they all work at the same rate).

ANSWER

As there are now eight florists, it will take them less than 4 hours. This means that the 4 hours should be multiplied by a fraction that is less than 1.

First, write out the fraction: $\frac{3 \text{ florists}}{8 \text{ florists}}$.
Then, multiply by the number of hours.

$$\frac{3}{8} \times 4 = \frac{12}{8} = 1.5 \text{ hours}$$

So, 8 florists would take **1.5 hours.**

Alternatively, you could multiply by 3 to calculate how long one florist would take and then divide by 8:

3 florists take 4 hours, so 1 florist would take $3 \times 4 = 12$ hours.

8 florists would take $\frac{12}{8}$ = **1.5 hours.**

COMMON MISTAKE

A common mistake here would be to calculate

$$4 \times \frac{8}{3} = \frac{32}{3} = 10\frac{2}{3}$$

thinking that with more florists the length of time would be greater.

WORKED EXAMPLE

If 12 workers in a warehouse can pack 160 boxes in 6 hours, then calculate how long it would take 9 workers, working at the same rate, to pack the same number of boxes.

ANSWER

As there are fewer employees, it will take them a longer time. This means that the 6 hours should be multiplied by a fraction that is greater than 1.

First write out the fraction of workers: $\frac{12}{9}$.
Then, multiply the time it takes for the 12 workers by this fraction:

$$6 \text{ hours} \times \frac{12}{9} = \frac{72}{9} = \textbf{8 hours}$$

Or, 12 workers take 6 hours, so 1 worker would take $6 \times 12 = 72$ hours

9 workers would take $\frac{72}{9}$ = **8 hours**

1 Ali is organising a reception party in a hall. He has chairs and tables in the ratio of 5 : 2.

   If he has 16 tables, then how many chairs does he need?

2 Laurenzo makes a fruit drink using the following recipe:
   –   170 mL lemonade
   –   90 mL orange juice
   –   70 mL tomato juice.

   He uses 175 mL of tomato juice.

   Calculate (in litres) the amount of fruit drink he will make.

3 9 taps fill a tank in three and a half hours.

   With the same water flow, calculate how long it would take 14 taps to fill the tank. Give your answer in hours and minutes.

1.12 Follow the order of precedence of operators, including indices

When carrying out calculations involving more than one operation, those operations must follow a particular order. That order is represented by the expression **BIDMAS**, which stands for **B**rackets, **I**ndices, **D**ivision, **M**ultiplication, **A**ddition, **S**ubtraction.

The term indices means to the power of. For example:

6^2 means 6 to the power of 2 (or 6 multiplied by itself): $6 \times 6 = $ **36**

4^3 means 4 to the power of 3: $4 \times 4 \times 4 = $ **64**

> **BIDMAS:** an acronym for the correct order of operations in calculations.
>
> **Indices:** shows how many times a number has to be multiplied by itself (also referred to as a power).

WORKED EXAMPLE

Calculate $5 \times 15 - (30 - 3^2)$

ANSWER

First, carry out the calculation in the brackets: $30 - 3^2 = 30 - 9 = 21$

So, $15 \times 5 - 21$

Now, there are two operations ($\times$ and $-$). Multiplication comes before subtraction in BIDMAS, so it is carried out next:

$15 \times 5 = 75$

$75 - 21 = $ **54**

COMMON MISTAKE

A common mistake is to carry out the addition first as it appears before the division i.e. $24 + 12 = 36$, then $36 \div 3 = 12$, which is incorrect. Following BIDMAS, division comes before addition, so $12 \div 3$ comes first.

CHECK YOUR UNDERSTANDING

1 Calculate $9 + 6^2 \div (10 - 1)$

2 Calculate $(13^2 - 5^2) \times 4 \div 8$

3 Calculate $\dfrac{(12 - 4 + 6)}{(11^2 - 7^2)} \times 6 - 1$

EXAM-STYLE QUESTIONS

Paper 1 Non-calculator questions

1 Write six hundred and twenty-one thousand and forty-four as a number. [1 mark]

2 Write the following number in words: 26,602. [1 mark]

3 Calculate $15 - 4 + 6 \div 2$ [2 marks]

4 Calculate 4.3×0.852 [2 marks]

5 Raphael has a mixture of red, green and blue counters in the ratio of $1 : 2 : 5$.

What fraction of the counters are green? [2 marks]

6 What fraction of £40 is £15? [2 marks]

7 A library buys a new computer. 60 people used the computer during the first week.

15% of the people used the computer on Tuesday and 25% used it on Thursday.

Complete the bar chart to show how many people used it on Tuesday and Thursday. [4 marks]

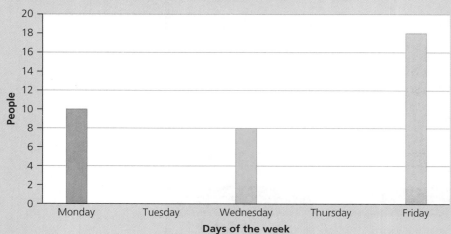

8 Calculate 12.5% of 34 kg. [2 marks]

9 Calculate 7.5% of 90 m. [2 marks]

10 A suit is reduced in price from £250 to £180 in a sale.

Johanna thinks this is a reduction of more than 30%. Is Johanna right? [3 marks]

11 A company records a profit of £388,454 in one year. This is an increase of £61,608 on the previous year.

   a Calculate the profit the company made in the previous year. [2 marks]

   b Show, by estimation, a check of your answer. [2 marks]

12 a Express 16 as a percentage of 25. [2 marks]

   b What percentage of 280 is 7? [2 marks]

13 In a year group of 208 students, 24 are studying both French and Spanish.

Express 24 as a fraction of 208. [2 marks]

14 There are 96 cars for sale in a garage. 18 are hybrid cars.

What fraction of the cars are **not** hybrid cars? [3 marks]

15 An airport records 201,000 people departing from it in one day.

Calculate, on average, how many people depart from the airport in one hour. [2 marks]

16 Alice is taking part in a 5 km park run. She has 760 m left to go.

What percentage of the run has she already completed? [3 marks]

17 A dress fabric is made up of different colours. 33% of the fabric is red, 26% blue, 13% yellow and the rest is green.

Calculate the fraction of the fabric that is green. [3 marks]

18 A tradesperson charges £45 an hour for their work plus a call out fee of £30.
The tradesperson works for 4 hours.

Calculate how much she would charge. [2 marks]

19 a   A decorator wants to make 40 L of purple paint by mixing red paint and blue paint in the ratio of 2 : 3. Calculate how much red paint and blue paint are needed. [3 marks]

b   The decorator needs more purple paint. She has 15 L of blue paint and 15 L of red paint. What is the maximum amount of purple paint she can make? [3 marks]

20 To make some black paint, a student mixes the three primary colours (blue, red and yellow) in the ratio of 4: 2 : 1. He uses 6 L of red paint. Calculate how much black paint will be made. [3 marks]

21 The angles BAC, ABC and ACB of a triangle are in the ratio of 10 : 7 : 3. Calculate the size of each angle. [4 marks]

> **MAKING LINKS**
>
> See Section 2.10 page 69 for more about the angles in a triangle.

22 Zeb and Dee win £320,000 in a lottery and share it in the ratio of 3 : 2. How much does Dee get? Choose from these answers: [1 mark]

A   £128,000

B   £64,000

C   £192,000

D   £160,000

23 Thirty-eight men and twenty-four women attend a presentation. Express the ratio of women to men in its simplest form. [2 marks]

24 The cost of a meal is divided between three friends, Sarah, Kelvin and Grace, in the ratio of 5 : 2 : 1. Kelvin pays £23. Calculate how much the other two pay. [3 marks]

25 Calculate $4\frac{2}{3} - 1\frac{7}{8}$ [3 marks]

26 A sum of money is divided between Maria and Phil in the ratio of 7 : 5. Phil receives £40. Calculate the total amount that they receive. [3 marks]

27 £87.50 is divided amongst three people, Azara, Anthony and Ezrah. Azara receives £52.50 and the rest is divided equally between Anthony and Ezrah. Calculate the fraction of the money that Anthony will receive. [3 marks]

28 Calculate $54 \div (58 - 7^2) \times 2$ [3 marks]

29 Express 40 as a fraction of 140. [2 marks]

30 Calculate $\frac{3}{7} - \frac{1}{3}$ [2 marks]

31 Calculate $\frac{7}{12} + \frac{5}{8}$ [2 marks]

32 It takes eight volunteers 10 hours to plant 100 trees. How long would it take for five volunteers to plant 100 trees, assuming they all work at the same rate? [1 mark]

    A 6.15 hours

    B 6 hours 25 minutes

    C 16 hours

    D 6 hours 15 minutes

33 Which fraction is 0.065 equivalent to? [1 mark]

    A $\dfrac{26}{40}$ **B** $\dfrac{13}{200}$ **C** $\dfrac{65}{100}$ **D** $\dfrac{13}{20}$

34 Sixty-two thousand, eight hundred and ninety-four people attended a football match. Fourteen thousand one hundred and twelve of those people were children.

    a Calculate how many adults attended the match. [2 marks]

    b Show, by estimation, a check of your answer. [2 marks]

35 A building company has 68 bags of cement each weighing 43 kg. Which of the following would be a suitable check (by estimation) of the calculation to find the total weight of the cement: [1 mark]

    A 2,800 ÷ 40 = 70   **C** 43 × 68 = 2900

    B 2924 ÷ 68 = 43   **D** 2720 ÷ 40 = 68

36 Write one hundred and nine thousand, eight hundred and seventy-four as a number. [1 mark]

37 Write the following numbers in numerical order from largest to smallest: [1 mark]

    903,626   792,000   −812,000   819,789   −851,629   −99,030

38 Owen's car insurance increases from £420 to £700. Calculate the percentage increase. [2 marks]

39 Place the following decimals in numerical order from largest to smallest: [1 mark]

    −0.086   0.806   −0.865   0.860   −0.806   0.868

40 A student measures the volume of water in a cylinder as three thousand, four hundred and sixty-seven and a half millilitres. Round this volume (in litres) to:

    a three decimal places. [1 mark]

    b two decimal places. [1 mark]

    c one decimal place. [1 mark]

41 Calculate:

    a 0.219 + 0.085 + 0.802 [2 marks]

    b 0.911 − 0.119 [2 marks]

    c 3.7 × 4.73 [2 marks]

    d 0.846 ÷ 0.12 [2 marks]

42 To calculate the area of a shape, a student uses the formula:

$$\frac{2ab+4ac}{2}$$

$a = 6\,\text{m}$, $b = 3.5\,\text{m}$ and $c = 1.5\,\text{m}$

Calculate the area of the shape. [2 marks]

Paper 2 Calculator questions

1 The value of an antique bought online for £1,860 increases by 7.7% over twelve months. Calculate by how much the value of the antique has increased. [2 marks]

2 Calculate:

   a 7% of £91 [2 marks]

   b 91% of £7. [2 marks]

3 Calculate 19.5% of 132 kg. [2 marks]

4 Mary buys a smartphone for £430. The value of the phone decreases by 14.2% over a year.

   Calculate the value of the phone after one year. [3 marks]

5 In a Black Friday sale, a pair of trainers is reduced by 40% to a price of £75.

   Calculate the original price of the trainers. [2 marks]

6 A smartphone is reduced by 15% from its original price to a sale price of a hundred and nineteen pounds.

   Calculate its original price. [2 marks]

7 Calculate the original price of a 3-piece suite which has been reduced by 45% in a sale to £770. [2 marks]

8 A car is sold for £7,800. This represents a depreciation in value to 60% of its original price.

   Calculate the original price of the car. [2 marks]

9 A book is bought in a sale at a discounted price of £14. The discount was 20%.

   Calculate its original price. [2 marks]

10 A woman sells her bitcoin for £42,000. This is 12% more than she originally bought the bitcoin for.

   Calculate the original value of her bitcoin. [2 marks]

11 A house is sold for 8% above its original price. It was sold for £378,000.

   Calculate its original price. [2 marks]

12 In an auction, a vase is sold for 80% above its original price.

   If it was sold for £4,500, calculate its original price. [2 marks]

13 Money is put into an account which pays 3% per annum. After one year there is £1,545.

   Calculate how much was initially put into the account. [2 marks]

14 In a survey on children's leisure, the ratio of the time the children spent indoors compared to outdoors was found to be 6 : 1.

   Calculate the percentage of their leisure time that the children spent outdoors. Give your answer to 3 decimal places. [3 marks]

15 The following diagram shows the dimensions of a classroom.

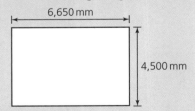

   Calculate:

   a The perimeter of the classroom (in m), [3 marks]

   b The area of the classroom (in m²), [3 marks]

   c The number of carpet tiles measuring 50 cm by 50 cm needed for the room. [3 marks]

16 Calculate 400 ÷ 27. Give your answer to:

    a   the nearest whole number   [1 mark]

    b   two decimal places.   [1 mark]

17 Sunita saves £1,500 towards the cost of a holiday costing £2,100.

    What percentage of the cost of the holiday has she already saved? Give your answer to one decimal place.   [3 marks]

18 In the following diagram, calculate how much of the circle is shaded, giving your answer as:

    a   a fraction   [1 mark]

    b   a decimal (to three decimal places)   [2 marks]

    c   a percentage (to one decimal place).   [2 marks]

19 Look at the two circles. Calculate how much of the circles are shaded combined.

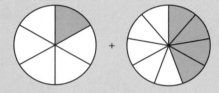

    Give your answer as:

    a   a fraction   [3 marks]

    b   a decimal (to three decimal places)   [2 marks]

    c   a percentage (to one decimal place).   [2 marks]

20 A café owner sells coffees. He charges £2.85 for a large cup, £2.50 for a medium-sized cup and £2.15 for a small cup. In a day he sells 24 large cups of coffee, 28 medium-sized cups and 25 small cups.

    Calculate how much income he receives from the sale of coffees in the day.   [4 marks]

21 Bennett and Margo want to work out the cost of their electricity bill. They check their meter reading every three months. The table below shows the current meter reading and the previous meter reading from three months ago.

Previous meter reading	92677
Current meter reading	95906

    The cost of one unit of electricity is 14.9p per kWh (kilowatt-hour). There is also a standing charge of £28.50 for three months to pay.

    Calculate the couple's bill.   [4 marks]

22 Place the following in order from smallest to largest: [1 mark]

    24.2%   0.402 $\frac{4}{21}$ $\frac{4}{22}$ 22.4%   0.244

23 Carys wants to buy an electric bike that costs £1,500. She has £1,100 saved.

Calculate how much she has left to save, as:

    a   a fraction (in its simplest form)   [2 marks]

    b   a decimal (to three decimal places)   [2 marks]

    c   a percentage (to one decimal place).   [2 marks]

24 Place the following in order from smallest to largest: [1 mark]

$$\frac{159}{13} \qquad 12\frac{1}{13} \qquad 13\frac{1}{12} \qquad \frac{145}{12} \qquad 13\frac{1}{13}$$

25 A sports shop is trialling five new brands of retro-trainer. The bar chart shows sales of the trainers during their first day on sale in the shop:

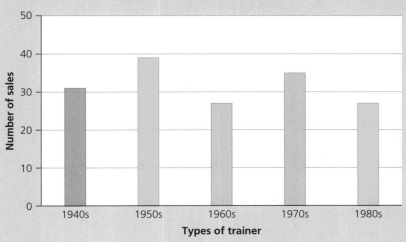

Calculate the percentage share of the most popular brand (to 2 decimal places).   [4 marks]

26 The area of the following trapezium is given by the formula .

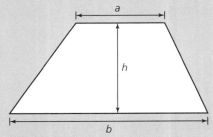

If $a = 2.5\,\text{cm}$, $b = 5.5\,\text{cm}$ and $h = 2.5\,\text{cm}$, calculate the area of the trapezium.   [3 marks]

2 Using common measures, shape and space

DIAGNOSTIC QUESTIONS

 Non-calculator questions

1   Look at the shape below. Calculate the shape's:

   a   perimeter

   b   area.

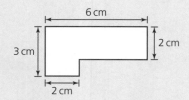

2   A man walks directly from A to B. Using a scale of 1 cm : 500 m calculate the distance (in km) he walks.

3   Sketch the net of a cube.

4   Draw a plan view of the 3-D shape below.

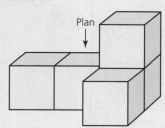

5   Calculate the angle x in the following isosceles triangle:

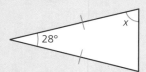

6   A man walks at an average speed of 3 miles per hour. Calculate how far he would walk in 45 minutes.

7   On the grid below, plot the co-ordinates (−2, 3), (3, −2) and (2, −3).

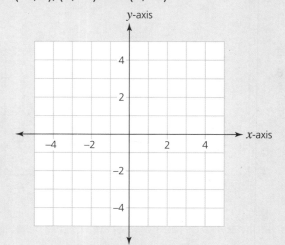

 Calculator questions

8   Look at the cylinder. Calculate its:

   a   volume

   b   the surface area (Take π = 3.14):

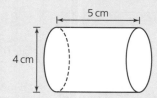

9   1 imperial gallon = 4.546 litres. Calculate how many imperial gallons there are in 5 litres. Give your answer to one decimal place.

10   There is a 15% discount on the cost of a rail ticket normally costing £128. Calculate the cost of the rail ticket after the discount has been applied.

2.1 Calculate amounts of money, compound interest, percentage increases, decreases and discounts including tax and simple budgeting

Calculating amounts of money: interest

Interest is the money received on savings kept in a bank or a building society. It is a percentage of the amount of money saved in the account.

When borrowing money, interest is paid on the amount borrowed (the loan). The interest paid is a percentage of the loan amount. This is known as the **interest rate**. Interest can be paid every year (annually) or every month.

WORKED EXAMPLE

A man has £650 in a savings account. The annual interest rate is 3%. Calculate the money he receives after interest after one year.

ANSWER

First convert 3% into a decimal: 3% = 0.03

Multiply the interest rate by the amount in the savings account: £650 × 0.03 = £19.50

The interest is added to the savings: £650 + £19.50 = **£669.50**

Alternatively, as 3% has been added on to the £650, then the money the man received is 103% of £650.
103% = 1.03.
So, £650 × 1.03 = **£669.50**

MAKING LINKS

For more on identifying and knowing the equivalence between fractions, decimals and percentages see Section 1.4, page 15.

Compound interest

When interest is added to an amount that has already had interest added to it, this is called compound interest.

> Compound interest: interest earned on an amount that already has interest added.

WORKED EXAMPLE

If the money and interest from the previous worked example is kept in the account (£669.50 with 3% interest), calculate the compound interest after the second year.

ANSWER

Take the interest + savings from question 1 and calculate the interest using that value.

669.50 × 0.03 = 20.085 = **£20.09** (to the nearest penny).

Discounts

A discount is a deduction from the usual cost of something. It can be expressed as a **percentage decrease**.

WORKED EXAMPLE

There is 37% discount on concert tickets that normally cost £85. Calculate the cost of a concert ticket after the discount.

ANSWER

When calculating percentage increases or percentage decreases, the percentage can first be changed to a decimal: 37% = 0.37

Find the discount amount: £85 × 0.37 = £31.45

Subtract the discount amount from the full price:
£85 − £31.45 = **£53.55**

Alternatively, 37% has been deducted from £85. So, 100% − 37% leaves 63%.

63% = 0.63.

So, £85 × 0.63 = **£53.55**

Calculating tax and budgeting

Tax is money that is paid to a government, used to pay for schools, hospitals, roads, emergency services, healthcare and so on. Salary or money earned before tax is taken is called gross income. Tax, like compound interest, is expressed as a **percentage increase**.

Simple budgeting involves making a record of your weekly (or monthly) spending on food, clothes, travel, bills and entertainment and balancing this against the amount of money that you earn or receive.

WORKED EXAMPLE

Johannes earns £33,240 a year. From his monthly salary, he pays 12% national insurance tax on his gross income and 20% income tax on the money he earns above his personal tax allowance (the amount of income he can earn or receive every year without paying income tax).

If his personal tax allowance is £12,570, calculate his monthly net pay (take-home pay) after income tax and national insurance have been deducted.

ANSWER

First, calculate the monthly gross salary: £33,240 ÷ 12 = £2,770

Calculate the amount of national insurance: £2,770 × 0.12 = £332.40

Calculate the money he earns above his personal tax allowance:
£33,240 − £12,570 = £20,670

Calculate the income tax amount: £20,670 × 0.2 = £4,134

Income tax amount per month: £4,134 ÷ 12 = £344.50

Add together the total deductions: £332.40 + £344.50 = £676.90

Net pay per month: £2,770 − £676.90 = **£2,093.10**

CHECK YOUR UNDERSTANDING

1   The cost of a pack of chipolata sausages in a local supermarket is £2.50. The cost increases by 42%.

Calculate the cost of the chipolata sausages after the percentage increase.

2   A woman invests £3,500 for two years in a bank with compound interest of 1.5% per annum (year).

Calculate the amount of interest she has earned after the two years.

3   Stephanie's monthly salary after tax is £1,950 per month. She pays £790 on rent and, on average, £380 per month on fuel and maintenance for her car. The table shows how much she spends on bills in a year.

Bill	Annual amount (£)
Electricity	2,910
Water	420
Internet/broadband	576

From the money remaining, she wants to set aside £150 per month towards a holiday. Calculate how much money she has left at the end of the month to spend on food, clothes and entertainment.

2.2 Convert between metric and imperial units of length, weight and capacity using a) a conversion factor and b) a conversion graph

REVISED

When you are asked to convert between metric and imperial units, or between imperial units and metric units, a conversion factor or a conversion graph will always be given.

Conversion factors

The table shows conversion factors between some common metric and imperial units:

Metric	1 kg	1 km	1 m	1 L
Imperial	2.2 lbs	0.62 miles	39.37 inches	0.22 gallons

WORKED EXAMPLE

A man runs 20 kilometres in training. Using the conversion 1 km = 0.62 miles, calculate how many miles he has run.

ANSWER

$$1\,km = 0.62\,miles$$
$$20\,km = ?$$

If the unit (1) is on the **left** side of the conversion and the unknown quantity (?) is on the **right** (as in this example), the two numbers pointed to by the double-headed arrow are multiplied:

So, 20 × 0.62

Without using a calculator, 20 can be 'split up' into 2 × 10.
So, 0.62 × 10 = 6.2.

Then, 2 × 6.2 = **12.4 km**

WORKED EXAMPLE

1 imperial gallon = 4.546 litres. Calculate the number of imperial gallons in 20.5 L. Give your answer to two decimal places.

ANSWER

$$1\text{ imperial gallon} = 4.546\,L$$
$$? = 20.5\,L$$

If the unit (1) is on the **left** side of the conversion and the unknown quantity (?) is on the **left** (as in this example), the two numbers pointed to by the double-headed arrow are divided.

The number below is divided by the number above:
20.5 ÷ 4.546 = **4.51 imperial gallons**

Conversion graphs

A conversion graph is used to convert a metric value into an imperial value or imperial value into a metric one, using horizontal and vertical lines on the graph.

WORKED EXAMPLE

Using the conversion graph, calculate how many gallons there are in 7 litres.

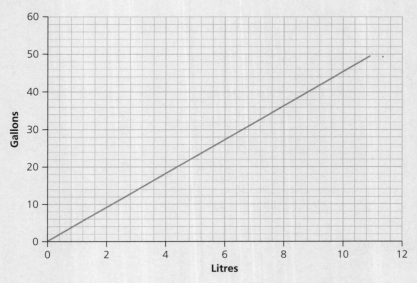

COMMON MISTAKE

A common mistake is to use the wrong axis when converting. It is important to find the correct axis for the unit being converted and then use the conversion line to read from the axis representing the other unit.

COMMON MISTAKE

A common mistake here would also be to misread the number on the vertical (gallons) axis as 31 or 30.1, instead of 32 by not realising that each division (gap between the lines) is two.

ANSWER

First, find 7 litres on the horizontal (litres) axis. Draw a vertical line up to the conversion line. At the point where the two lines meet, draw a horizontal line across to the vertical (gallons) axis.

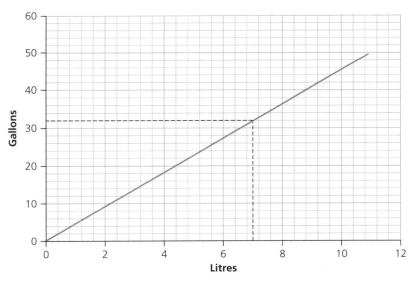

Read the number off the scale: **32 gallons**.

1 A man's suitcase weighs 3 stone before he goes to the airport. He will have to pay for excess baggage if his suitcase weighs more than 20 kg. Using the conversion graph, find out if he will have to pay for excess baggage for his flight. (1 stone = 14 lbs).

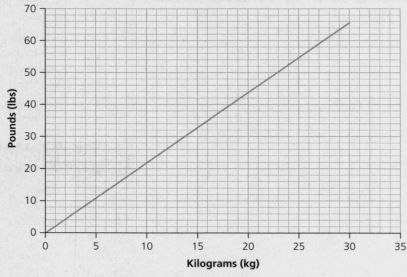

 2 1 imperial gallon = 4.546 litres. Calculate:

    a   the number of litres in 33 imperial gallons.

    b   the number of imperial gallons in 20,500 mL. Give your answer to two decimal places.

 3 A company has designed a robot. The robot is 5 foot 2 inches, weighs 9 stone and can walk at 3 miles per hour. Using the following conversions, calculate:

    a   Its speed in kilometres per hour (1 mile/hour = 1.6 km/hour).

    b   Its height in metres (1 inch = 2.5 cm and 1 foot = 12 inches).

    c   Its weight in kilograms (1 stone = 14 pounds and 2.2 pounds = 1 kg).

2.3 Calculate using compound measures including speed, density and rates of pay

Compound measures are measures with more than one quantity. They require more than one unit.

> **Compound measure:** a measure that has more than one quantity, e.g. speed, density or rate of pay.

Calculating speed and density

Speed is calculated by dividing distance by time. It is measured in miles per hour (miles/h) or km per hour (km/h).

$$\text{speed} = \frac{\text{distance}}{\text{time}}$$

Density is calculated by dividing the mass of an object by its volume. It is usually measured in grams per cubic centimetre (g/cm^3).

$$\text{density} = \frac{\text{mass}}{\text{volume}}$$

Calculating rates of pay

Rate of pay may be measured in £/hour or £/week or given as a monthly salary (£/month) or annual salary (£/year). It can be calculated by dividing the money earned by the length of time taken to earn that money.

$$\text{rate of pay} = \frac{\text{money earned}}{\text{time taken to earn money}}$$

When doing calculations, it's important to focus on using the correct units.

WORKED EXAMPLE

A woman walks 11 miles in 2 hours and 30 minutes. Calculate her average speed.

ANSWER

distance = 11 miles

time = 2 hours 30 minutes (2 hours 30 mins = 2.5 hours)

Use the formula and put in the values:

$$\text{speed} = \frac{\text{distance}}{\text{time}} = \frac{11}{2.5} \times \frac{\times 2}{\times 2} = \frac{22}{5}$$

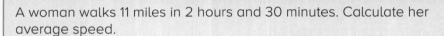

$$5\overline{)22.^20} \quad \begin{array}{c} 4.\ 4 = \textbf{4.4 miles/hour} \end{array}$$

EXAM TIP

Use the units given to help determine the formula. For example, density (g/cm^3), grams is a unit of mass and cm^3 is a unit of volume. With speed (km/h), kilometres is a unit of distance and hours is a unit of time.

WORKED EXAMPLE

A block of steel of density 7.79 g/cm³ measures 0.2 m by 0.05 m by 0.05 m. Calculate its mass (in kilograms).

ANSWER

We need the formula: $density = \dfrac{mass}{volume}$

However, to calculate mass the formula needs to be rearranged. Rearranged, the formula is:

$$mass = density \times volume$$

First, calculate the volume. As the unit of density is g/cm³, volume needs to be calculated in cm³. The dimensions of the block should be converted from m to cm:

0.2 m = 20 cm; 0.05 m = 5 cm

Volume in cm³ = 20 cm × 5 cm × 5 cm = 100 × 5 = 500 cm³

Therefore mass = 7.79 g/cm³ × 500 cm³ = 3,895 g = **3.895 kg**

CHECK YOUR UNDERSTANDING

 1   A person drives his car at an average speed of 50 miles per hour. Calculate the distance he has travelled after two and three-quarter hours.

 2   A man is offered a similar job at his current company, which pays £15 a week less. However, he can work from home two out of five days a week. His workplace is 19 miles from his home. His car travels 10 miles per litre of diesel. Diesel costs £1.83 per litre.
Will the man be better off with his new job after he takes the cost of travel into consideration? Include calculations to support your answer.

 3   A silver necklace has a mass of 0.0285 kg. The density of silver is 10.49 g/cm³. Calculate the necklace's volume in cubic centimetres. Give your answer to three decimal places.

2.4 Calculate perimeters and areas of 2-D shapes including triangles and circles and composite shapes including non-rectangular shapes

Calculating perimeter

The perimeter of a two-dimensional shape is the distance around that shape. For example, a triangle has three sides, so its perimeter will be the total distance (or sum) of the three sides:

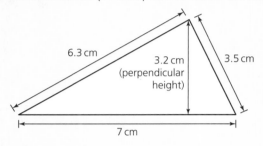

perimeter of triangle = 7 cm + 6.3 cm + 3.5 cm = **16.8 cm**

A parallelogram has four sides, so its perimeter will be the total distance (or sum) of the four sides:

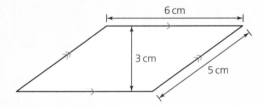

perimeter of parallelogram = (6 cm + 5 cm) × 2 = 11 cm × 2 = **22 cm**

Calculating the circumference

The perimeter of a circle is called its circumference. The ratio between the circumference of a circle and its diameter is known as pi **(π)**. Pi is a neverending number and has the approximate value of 3.14. The centre of the circle to the circumference is the radius.

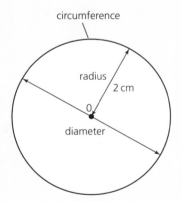

The circumference of a circle = pi × diameter (πd) or 2 × pi × radius ($2\pi r$).

In the circle diagram above, radius = 2 cm and diameter = 4 cm

So, circumference = πd = 3.14 × 4 = **12.56 cm**

> **Perimeter:** the distance around a shape.
>
> **Circumference:** the total distance around a circle.
>
> **Radius:** a straight line from the centre of a circle to any point on its circumference.
>
> **Diameter:** a straight line from any point on the circumference through the centre (O) to the opposite end of the circumference.
>
> **Pi:** a mathematical constant; the ratio of a circle's circumference to its diameter (approximately 3.14).

> **EXAM TIP**
>
> The circumference of a circle is always just over three times its diameter and the diameter of a circle is always twice its radius.

Calculating area

The area of a two-dimensional shape is a measure of the space inside that shape. It is measured in square units, usually centimetres squared (cm^2) or metres squared (m^2).

For example, to calculate the area of this square, its two dimensions (length and width) are multiplied:

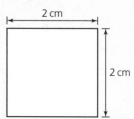

Area of square = $2\,cm \times 2\,cm = 4\,cm^2$

Calculating the area of a parallelogram
The area of a parallelogram is calculated from the formula:

length of base of parallelogram × height of parallelogram

So, the area of this parallelogram: $6 \times 3 = \textbf{18 cm}^2$

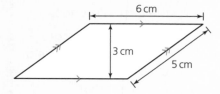

Calculating the area of a trapezium
The area of a trapezium is calculated from the formula:

$\frac{1}{2}$ (sum of parallel sides of trapezium) × height of trapezium

So, the area of the trapezium here: $\frac{1}{2} \times (4 + 2) \times 3.5 = \textbf{10.5 cm}^2$

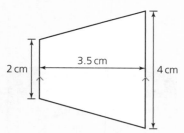

Calculating the area of a triangle
The area of a triangle is calculated from the formula:

$\frac{1}{2}$ base of triangle × perpendicular height from the base

So, the area of this triangle is: $\frac{7.3 \times 3.2}{2} = \textbf{11.2 cm}^2$

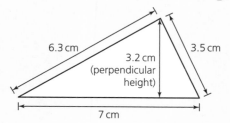

EXAM TIP

The base of a parallelogram will always be its longer side.

COMMON MISTAKE

Be careful not to multiply the base by a dimension other than the perpendicular height of the triangle from the base (i.e. 3.5 cm or 6.3 cm instead of 3.2 cm). Make sure you only multiply two dimensions and not three dimensions.

Calculating the area of a circle

The area of a circle is calculated from the formula:

pi × radius squared (or πr^2)

So, the area of this circle: $3.14 \times 2 \times 2 = \textbf{12.56 cm}^2$

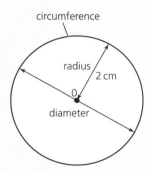

WORKED EXAMPLE

The following **composite shape** consists of a semi-circle on top of a square. Calculate:

   a its perimeter

   b its area.

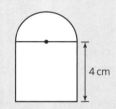

4 cm

ANSWER

  a First, calculate the perimeter of the square. Only the lines on the **outside** of the shape should be included, of which there are three.

     So, perimeter of three sides of the square: 4 cm × 3 = **12 cm**

     Then calculate the circumference of the semi-circle. As squares have four equal sides, the diameter of the semi-circle = 4 cm

     The circumference of a circle = πd. A semi-circle has half the circumference of a circle so the length needed is $\frac{\pi d}{2}$

$$\frac{\pi d}{2} = \frac{4 \times 3.14}{2} = \frac{12.56}{2} = 6.28 \text{ cm}$$

     Add the perimeter of the square and circumference of the semi-circle:

     12 cm + 6.28 cm = **18.28 cm**

  b Area of the shape = area of semi-circle + area of the square

     Area of semi-circle $= \dfrac{\pi r^2}{2}$

     So, area of shape $= \dfrac{\pi r^2}{2} + (4 \times 4) = \dfrac{3.14 \times 2 \times \cancel{2}}{\cancel{2}} + 16$

                           $= \textbf{22.28 cm}^2$

> **Composite shape**: a 2-D shape made from a combination of other 2-D shapes.

> **COMMON MISTAKE**
>
> In this question, do not include all four sides of the square when calculating the perimeter. One of the sides, the top of the square is an internal line and not part of the perimeter.

> **EXAM TIP**
>
> If you make an error in your workings (for example, using the radius instead of the diameter, or vice-versa), but follow through to obtain the correct answer for that mistake, then 'method marks' can still be awarded. So, it's always worth attempting questions.

1 The diagram represents a piece of land in the shape of an equilateral triangle. Concrete posts are placed around the land at 1.5 m intervals. Calculate the number of posts needed.

8.5 m

 2 The composite shape represents a plan view of a garden in the form of a rectangle and an isosceles triangle. Calculate:

a its perimeter

b its area.

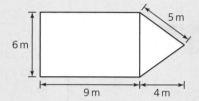

 3 The diagram represents a garden in the shape of three quarters of a circle. A bag of fertiliser covers 15 m² of the garden and costs £11.95 a bag. There is currently 'buy one, get one free' offer on bags of fertiliser.

Calculate the cost of the fertiliser. (Take π = 3.14)

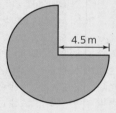

4.5 m

2.5 Use formulae to find volumes and surface areas of 3-D shapes including cylinders

REVISED

Calculating the volume of 3-D shapes

The volume of any 3-D shape is a measure of the space inside it. You are expected to know the formula for calculating the volume of a cuboid, cube or cylinder.

Volume is measured in cubic units, usually cubic centimetres (cm^3) or cubic metres (m^3).

The volume of cuboids and prisms can be calculated by multiplying the base area of the shape by its height.

> **COMMON MISTAKE**
>
> Be careful when you write units for volume. It is a common mistake for students to put the wrong unit in the answer e.g. cm, or cm^2, instead of cm^3.

WORKED EXAMPLE

This cuboid has a base area of $15\,cm^2$ and a height of $3\,cm$. Calculate the volume of the cuboid.

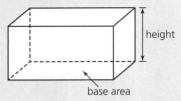

ANSWER

The volume of the cuboid:

Volume = base area × height

$\qquad$ = $15\,cm^2 \times 3\,cm$

$\qquad$ = **45 cm^3**

> **EXAM TIP**
>
> For other common 3-D shapes (e.g. spheres, square-based pyramids and cones) the volume can be calculated from a given formula.

Calculating the volume of a cylinder

The volume of a cylinder is calculated by multiplying the area of one of its ends (πr^2), by the height of the cylinder (h).

The height of a cylinder is the perpendicular height from the base of the cylinder to the top of the cylinder.

So, volume of a cylinder = $\pi r^2 h$

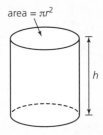

area = πr^2

Calculating the surface area of 3-D shapes

Calculating surface area of cylinders

A solid cylinder has two faces (at its ends) and one curved surface. Its two ends each have an area of πr^2, so the area of the two ends of the cylinder = $2\pi r^2$.

If the curved surface of the cylinder was 'unrolled', it would form a rectangle.

The length would be the circumference of the circle (πd or $2\pi r$) and the height of which would be h.

So, the area of the curved surface = πdh

Total surface area of cylinder = $\pi dh + 2\pi r^2$

> **Surface area:** a measure of the total surface area of all the exterior parts of a shape. The units used for measuring surface area are m^2, cm^2, $inches^2$ etc.

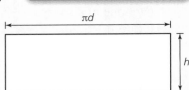

πd

h

WORKED EXAMPLE

A cylindrical footstool is 0.5 m high and has a diameter of 40 cm.

Calculate the footstool's:

    a   volume

    b   surface area.

       (Take π = 3.14)

> ### ANSWER
>
> First, convert the height of the footstool from m to cm: 0.5 m = 50 cm
>
> Then calculate the radius of the footstool: 40 cm ÷ 2 = 20 cm
>
>   **a**   Volume of footstool = π × radius squared × height = $\pi r^2 h$
>
> $$= 3.14 \times 20^2 \times 50 = \mathbf{62{,}800\ cm^3}$$
>
>   **b**   Surface area = (π × diameter × height) + (2π × radius squared)
>
> $$= \pi dh + 2\pi r^2$$
>
> $$= (3.14 \times 40 \times 50) + (2 \times 3.14 \times 20^2)$$
>
> $$= 6{,}280 + 2{,}512 = \mathbf{8{,}792\ cm^2}$$

CHECK YOUR UNDERSTANDING

1   The diagram shows a square-based pyramid. Calculate its volume.

    (Volume of a square-based pyramid $= \frac{1}{3} \times$ base area × height)

2   Calculate the surface area of a cylinder with a height (from its base) of 0.45 m and a radius of 19 cm.

    Give your answer in square metres, to 1 decimal place.

    (Take π = 3.14)

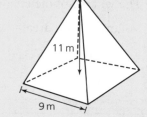

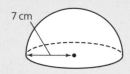

3   The diagram below is a hemisphere of radius 7 cm.

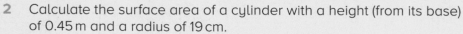

    Calculate the hemisphere's:

   a   volume

   b   surface area.

    Give your answers to the nearest whole number.

    (Volume of a sphere $= \frac{4}{3}\pi r^3$ and the surface area of a sphere $= 4\pi r^2$)

    (Take π = 3.14)

2.6 Calculate actual dimensions from scale drawings and create a scale diagram given actual measurements

A scale diagram is a proportional, two-dimensional drawing that represents something in real life, for example, a plan of a room or a garden, or a map of a local area.

The scale on a scale diagram tells us how many times larger or smaller an object is. Scale drawings can represent objects that are larger or smaller than the actual object.

For example, a scale of 1 cm : 5 m means that 1 cm on the drawing represents 5 m in real life. As 1 m = 100 cm, we can also write the scale as 1 cm : 500 cm. Then, as the same unit is on both sides, we can write the scale as 1 : 500.

> **Scale diagram:** a proportional 2-D drawing of a real-life object.

Calculating actual dimensions from scale drawings

> **WORKED EXAMPLE**
>
> 1 cm on a scale drawing represents 4 km in real life.
>
> Calculate how far 4 cm on the scale drawing would represent in real life.
>
> > **ANSWER**
> >
> > A scale is a ratio, so when using a scale to find a dimension (scale drawing dimension or real life dimension), do the same to both sides of the scale.
> >
> > Write out the ratio: Scale drawing : Real life
> >
> > Fill in the values:
> >
> >
> >
> > Here, both sides are multiplied by 4 to calculate what 4 cm on a scale drawing represents in real life.

> **MAKING LINKS**
>
> Ratios are covered in more detail in Section 1.11, page 35.

> **EXAM TIP**
>
> When working with scales, it is good practice to write the scale down and (as with ratios) do the calculations underneath.

> **EXAM TIP**
>
> If a scale has no units, the same unit can be given to both sides of the scale ratio. For example, a scale of 1 : 2500 can be written as 1 cm : 2500 cm
>
> 1 cm : 25 m
>
> This then can make it easier to calculate actual dimensions from the scale.

Creating a scale diagram from actual measurements

A garden measures 12 m in length by 8 m in width. Using a scale of 1 : 200, draw a scale diagram of the garden.

COMMON MISTAKE

Make sure you use the correct dimensions when you label your scale drawing. Use the real-life dimensions, not the scale dimensions.

ANSWER

First, write the scale:

Scale drawing : Real life

1 : 200

Give the scale units

1 cm : 200 cm

Convert the real-life dimension from cm to m and fill in the values:

Length

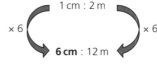

Width

So, the 12 m length is represented by a 6 cm line and the 8 m width is represented by a 4 cm line.

Draw the scale dimensions on a centimetre grid. Label the dimensions as the real-life dimensions.

12 m (length)

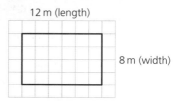

8 m (width)

CHECK YOUR UNDERSTANDING

1   Tom measures the distance between two towns on a map as 7 cm. If the scale is 2 cm : 5 km, calculate the distance between the two towns (include units).

2   Using a scale of 1 cm to represent 50 m, draw a line that would represent a half of a kilometre on a scale drawing.

3   It takes a man 30 mins to walk directly from A to B. He walks at an average speed of 4 km/hour.

   a   Calculate a suitable scale for the line shown.

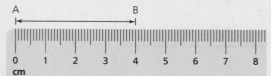

   b   Convert the scale in part **a** to a scale without units.

2.7 Use coordinates in 2-D, positive and negative, to specify the positions of points

Using 2-D coordinates

A point on a grid can be determined by its coordinates. When plotting points on a grid, the first number always represents x (the horizontal axis of the grid) and the second number represents y (the vertical axis of the grid).

If the y-value of a coordinate is negative, the coordinate will be below the x-axis. If the x-value of a coordinate is negative, then the coordinate will be to the left of the y-axis.

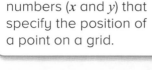

Coordinate: two numbers (x and y) that specify the position of a point on a grid.

Look at the grid below:

- To plot the point (3, 2), find 3 on the x-axis then go up to 2 on the y-axis. Plot the point (3, 2) at that point with a cross or a dot.

- To plot the point (−1, 4), find −1 on the x-axis, then go up to 4 on the y-axis. Plot the point (−1, 4) at that point with a cross or a dot.

- To plot the point (−2, −4) find −2 on the x-axis, then go down to −4 on the y-axis. Plot the point (−2, −4) at that point with a cross or a dot.

- To plot the point (2, −2), find 2 on the x-axis, then go down to −2 on the y-axis. Plot the point (2, −2) at that point with a cross or a dot.

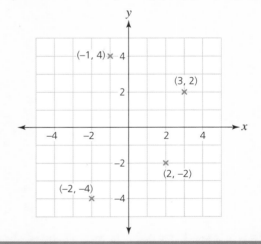

WORKED EXAMPLE

State the coordinates of the points A and B on this grid.

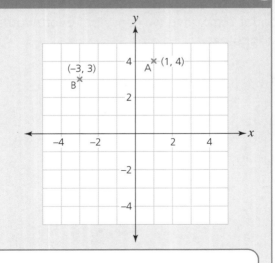

COMMON MISTAKE

Be careful not to get the coordinates the wrong way round and write (4, 1) instead of (1, 4) or (3, −3) instead of (−3, 3). The x-axis number goes first, then the y-axis number.

ANSWER

A = **(1, 4)**   B = **(−3, 3)**

1   Look at the grid. Write the coordinates of points A, B, C and D.

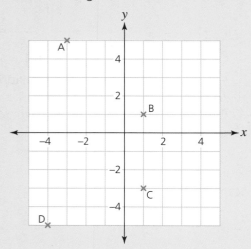

2   **a**   On the grid below, plot points at coordinates (−4, −2), (−2, 2) and (5, 2).
    b   The three points from part **a** are three corners of a parallelogram. Plot the point at the fourth corner and complete the parallelogram.

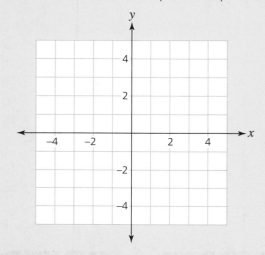

3   On the grid below, there are points at coordinates (−1, −3) and (3, −3). When a third point is added, they make the shape of a right-angled triangle with an area of 12 cm². Taking one square on the grid to equal 1 cm², give two possible coordinates for the third point. Draw the right-angled triangles.

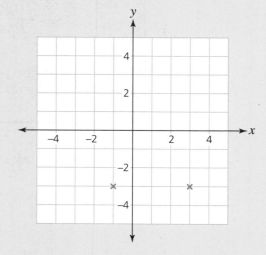

2.8 Understand and use common 2-D representations of 3-D objects

2-D drawings can be used to represent 3-D shapes that we see in everyday life, such as boxes, cones, cylinders and spheres.

2-D shapes are two-dimensional, flat, plane shapes, whereas 3-D shapes have three dimensions: length, width and depth. Looking at a 2-D representation of a 3-D object, we should be able to identify it – for example, tell where the faces of the object are, where the vertices (corners) are, whether it has any lines of symmetry and where the base of the object is.

From a 2-D representation, we can work out a shape's volume and/or surface area. With a diagram of a cone, for example, given its radius and height, we can work out its volume and/or surface area.

Nets

To gain a clearer understanding of a 3-D object, a 2-D representation of the object can be drawn in the form of a **net**. A net is the pattern made when a 3-D object is unfolded along its edges so that each face of the object is shown in two dimensions.

> **MAKING LINKS**
>
> For more on volumes and surface areas of 3-D shapes, see Section 2.5, page 59.

> **Net**: what a 3-D object would look like if it was opened out and laid out flat.

WORKED EXAMPLE

Draw a net of this cylinder:

ANSWER

In the net below, the cylinder has been 'unfolded' to show the top and bottom faces of the cylinder (the two circles), above and below the curved face (the rectangle) of the cylinder.

> **EXAM TIP**
>
> The 'net' of the cylinder shows the parts that make up the cylinder. This can assist in working out its surface area (see Section 2.5).

1   Look at the 2-D representation of a cone. The diameter of the cone at its base is 22 cm and its height is 22 cm.
    Calculate the cone's volume to the nearest cubic centimetre.
    (Volume of a cone $= \frac{1}{3}\pi r^2 h$)

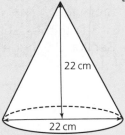

22 cm

22 cm

2   Sketch a net of a square-based pyramid.

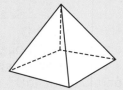

3   The following are nets of 3-D shapes. Name the shapes.
    a   b   c

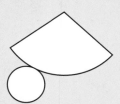

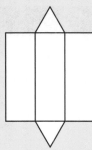

2.9 Draw 3-D shapes to include plans and elevations

When drawing a 3-D shape, what you show depends on the position you are looking at the shape from.

The view from the top is called the plan. The view from the front and sides are called the elevations (front elevation and side elevation).

> **Plan view**: a 2-D drawing of a 3-D shape as seen from above the shape.
>
> **Front elevation**: a 2-D drawing of a 3-D shape as seen from the front of the shape.
>
> **Side elevation**: a 2-D drawing of a 3-D shape as seen from the side of a shape.

WORKED EXAMPLE

Draw a plan view, front elevation and side elevation of the three-dimensional shape below.

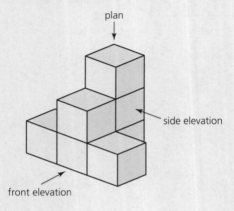

plan

side elevation

front elevation

ANSWER

For each drawing, consider the position you are looking at the object from, then how many squares (or units) there are going across and how many there are going up.

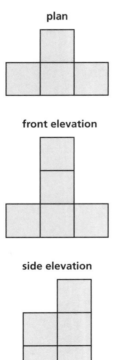

plan

front elevation

side elevation

COMMON MISTAKE

A common mistake here is to include more parts of the object in the plan and/or elevations than there actually are.

CHECK YOUR UNDERSTANDING

1   Below is a diagram of a cube. Draw:
   a   a plan view
   b   a front elevation
   c   a side elevation of the cube.

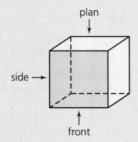

3   Look at the 3-D object below, and draw:
   a   a plan view
   b   a front elevation
   c   a side elevation.

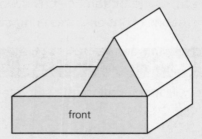

2   Look at the 3-D object here, and draw:
   a   a plan view
   b   a front elevation
   c   a side elevation.

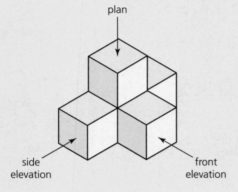

2.10 Calculate values of angles and/or coordinates with 2-D and 3-D shapes

Calculating values of angles in 2-D shapes

Angles in triangles

In a triangle, the sum of the three angles is always 180°.

Equilateral triangle	Isosceles triangle	Scalene triangle
All three angles (and sides) are equal (60°).	Two angles (and two sides) are equal.	All three angles and sides are different.
$60° + 60° + 60° = \mathbf{180°}$	$70° + 70° + 40° = \mathbf{180°}$	$40° + 60° + 80° = \mathbf{180°}$

Angles in parallelograms

In a parallelogram (and all quadrilaterals), the sum of the four angles will be 360°.

In the parallelogram here: $60° + 120° + 60° + 120° = 360°$

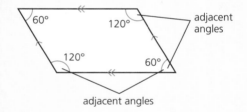

adjacent angles

adjacent angles

> **EXAM TIP**
>
> It's also important to know, when calculating angles, that there are 180° in a straight line.

Opposite angles in a parallelogram are equal and the sum of **any two** of its **adjacent angles will be** equal to **180°**.

$120° + 60° = 180°$

WORKED EXAMPLE

Look at the triangle. Calculate the size of the angle shown as $x°$.

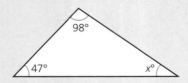

> **ANSWER**
>
> There are 180° in a triangle.
>
> $47° + 98° = 145°$
>
> So, $180° - 145° = 35°$
>
> $x° = \mathbf{35°}$

WORKED EXAMPLE

Calculate the sizes of angles *a* and *b* in the parallelogram.

ANSWER

Opposite angles of a parallelogram are equal:

$a° = $ **58°**

Angles *a* and *b* are adjacent so their sum will be 180°:

$b° = 180° - 58° = $ **122°**

A parallelogram's four angles add up to 360°. So, the calculation can be checked by adding up the four angles.
$58° + 122° + 58° + 122° = 360°$

Calculating values of angles in 3-D shapes

Knowledge of 2-D shapes can be used to calculate angles in 3-D shapes.

WORKED EXAMPLE

In the following 2-D representation of a square-based pyramid on a cuboid, the triangular faces of the pyramid are isosceles triangles.

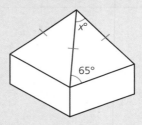

Calculate the angle *x*.

ANSWER

$65° + 65° = 130°$ (angles at the base of an isosceles triangle are equal).

$x° = 180° - 130° = $ **50°** (angles in a triangle add up to 180°)

Calculating values of coordinates with 2-D and 3-D shapes

Knowledge of 2-D and 3-D shapes can be used to calculate the value of coordinates. Through plotting the coordinates of 2-D and 3-D shapes on a grid, the coordinates of other points on the shape can be calculated.

WORKED EXAMPLE

On the following grid, A (−2, −1), B (−2, 2) and C (3, 2) are three corners on the face of a cuboid.

Calculate the coordinate of the fourth corner of the face of the cuboid.

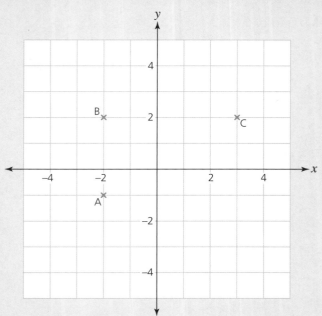

ANSWER

First, connect A to B and B to C. Then, calculate how many squares it is across from A to the x-coordinate of C (5 squares), and how many squares it is down from C to the y-coordinate of A (3 squares). Then, plot the coordinate **(3, −1)**.

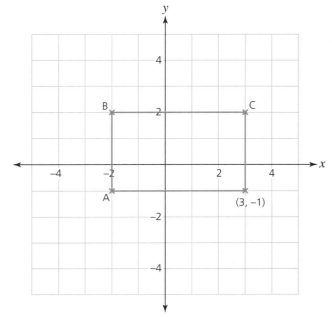

1   Look at the triangle. Calculate the value of y.

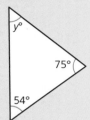

2   In the following parallelogram, calculate angles p and q.

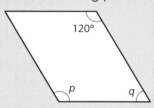

3   Four points on a grid form one side of a cube. The coordinates of
    three of the points are (–2, 4), (4, 4) and (4, –2).

    a   Using the grid below, plot the four points.

    b   Calculate the volume of the cube.

    c   Calculate the surface area of the cube.

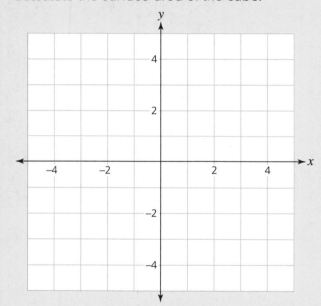

EXAM-STYLE QUESTIONS

Paper 1 Non-calculator questions

1 Which of the following shows a net of a cone? [1 mark]

 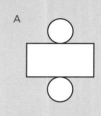 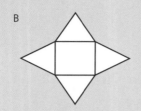 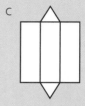 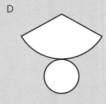

2 Which of these 3-D shapes will have:

  a more than one right angle at its base? [1 mark]

  b the same number of vertices as faces? [1 mark]

    i triangular prism

    ii cube

    iii triangular-based pyramid

    iv cone.

3 Look at the 3-D object.

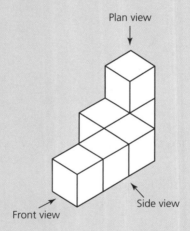

Match each of the views with one of the following diagrams. [1 mark]

A   B   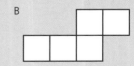   C   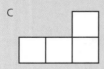   D   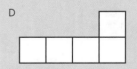

4 Ezatullah cycles 45 km at an average speed of 20 km/h.

Calculate how long it would take him. Give your answer in hours and minutes. [3 marks]

5 The sculpture 'Dignity', in South Dakota, USA, is 50 feet tall. Given that
1 inch = 2.5 cm, calculate its height in metres (1 foot = 12 inches). [2 marks]

6 A woman walks 5 km in 1 hour 15 minutes. Calculate her average speed. [2 marks]

7 Stephen drives 192 kilometres at an average speed of 50 miles per hour.

Calculate the time he takes. Give your answer in hours and minutes. (1 mile = 1.6 km) [4 marks]

8 The following diagram shows the net of a 3-D shape. Name the shape and draw a plan view of it. [3 marks]

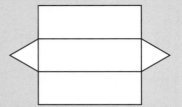

9 a In this parallelogram, the longer side is twice the length of the shorter side. Calculate its perimeter. [2 marks]

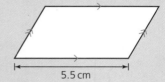

5.5 cm

b In this isosceles triangle, the long side is three times the length of the base. Calculate its perimeter. [2 marks]

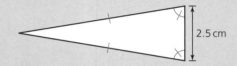

2.5 cm

10 The diagram below is an isosceles triangle. Calculate angle *x*. [2 marks]

x°

140°

11 Using a scale of 1 : 250,000 draw a line that would represent a distance of 20 km on a scale drawing. [3 marks]

12 Look at the images of a model dinosaur, and a model house and garage. Using the conversion graph, calculate their lengths in centimetres. Then, using the scales given complete the table. [4 marks]

4 inches

2.8 inches

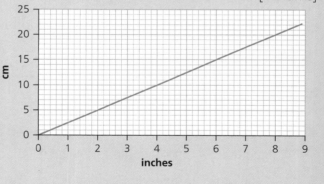

	Inches	cm	Scale	Real life size (m)
Model dinosaur	4		1 : 150	
Model house and garage	2.8		1 : 300	

13 Look at the following parallelogram:

What value is angle *a*? Circle the correct answer. [1 mark]

A ½*x*

B 180° + *x*

C 180° − *x*

D *x*

14 A woman cycles from A to B to C at an average speed of 30 km/h. If the scale used on the diagram below is 1 : 250,000, calculate the time taken. [4 marks]

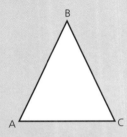

15 a 12 cm on a scale drawing represents 0.6 km in real life. Calculate the scale used. [2 marks]

   b John argues that the scale used is the same as 4 : 20,000.

   Is he correct? Give a reason for your answer. [2 marks]

16 Using a scale of 1 cm : 20 cm, calculate what distance on a scale drawing would represent 1.2 m in real life. [1 mark]

17 Nigella is using a map to find her new local bank. The scale is 1 : 20,000. Following the route on the map below, how far does she have to walk from her home to the bank? Give your answer in km. [3 marks]

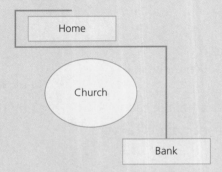

18 A pane of glass measures 80 cm by 50 cm. Using a scale of 1 : 20, draw a scale diagram of the pane of glass. [3 marks]

19 A man walks directly from C to D. Using a scale of 1 : 25,000 calculate the distance he walks. Give your answer in kilometres. [3 marks]

C ——————————————————————— D

20 If 20 units on a scale drawing represent 400 units in real life, calculate the scale used for the drawing. [2 marks]

21 A man earns £23,840 per annum. Calculate how much he gets paid per month. [2 marks]

22 Look at the 3-D object below, and draw:

    a   a plan view   [2 marks]

    b   a front elevation   [2 marks]

    c   a side elevation.   [2 marks]

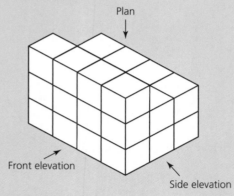

23 On the grid below:

    a   Plot the points P (−5, 3), Q (−3, 5) and R (0, 2).   [3 marks]

    b   Plot one more point on the grid, to make a rectangle. Label the points S and show its coordinates.   [2 marks]

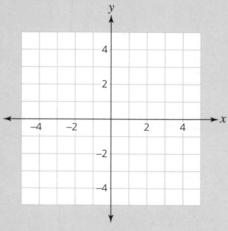

24 On the grid below:

    a   Plot the points A (−2,4) and B (3,4). Plot a third points to make a right-angled, isosceles triangle, with the x-coordinate as a positive integer. Label this point C.   [4 marks]

    b   Taking one square on the grid to equal 1cm², calculate the area of the triangle.   [2 marks]

    c   Mamuni thinks that the perimeter of the triangle is ≤15 cm. Is she correct? Give a reason for your answer.   [2 marks]

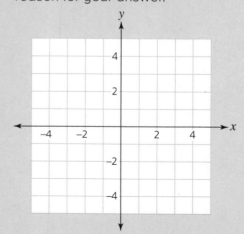

25 Look at the 2-D representation of a triangular prism. [3 marks]

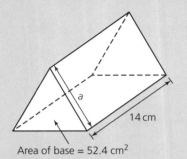

14 cm

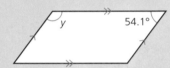
Area of base = 52.4 cm^2

Calculate its volume.

Paper 2 Calculator questions

1 Pareesa earns £11.31 an hour. How much would she earn in 37.5 hours? [1 mark]

  A £424.13

  B £424.15

  C £424

  D £424.12

2 Calculate the value of y in the following parallelogram. [2 marks]

y 54.1°

3 A suit normally costing £72 is reduced by 32% in a sale. The shop manager wants the sale price to be to the nearest pound. Which of the following prices should the suit be sold for? [1 mark]

  A £47

  B £48

  C £49

  D £50

4 A woman earns 3.5% compound interest per annum on her savings of £2,000. How much does she have in the account after **two** years? [3 marks]

5 After her holiday, a woman wishes to change one hundred euros back to British pounds. Using the exchange rate of £1 = €1.17, calculate how many pounds she would get. [2 marks]

6 A piece of wood furniture has a mass of 24.2 pounds and volume of 22,000 cm^3. Calculate the density of a piece.

$$\text{density} = \frac{\text{mass}}{\text{volume}}$$

Use the conversion 1kg = 2.2 pounds and give the units in g/cm^3. [3 marks]

7 Two friends go to South Africa for a holiday. Ahmed travels from the UK with British pounds, while Kirk travels from Germany with euros.

They both exchange their money for South African rand when they arrive in South Africa. The table shows the exchange rates.

1 pound (£)	20.54 South African rand
1 euro (€)	18.08 South African rand

Ahmed spends 22,500 rand and has 3,175 rand left over at the end of the holiday, while Kirk spends 23,000 rand and has 2,764 rand left over. Calculate:

  a How many pounds Ahmed exchanged at the beginning of the holiday. [3 marks]

  b How many euros Kirk exchanged at the beginning of the holiday. [3 marks]

8 If 1L = 35.2 imperial fluid ounces, calculate how many litres (to one decimal place) there are in 1,000 imperial fluid ounces. [2 marks]

9 If a farmer has 100 acres of land, calculate this area in hectares, to three decimal places. (1 acre = 4,046.86 m^2, 1 hectare = 10,000 m^2) [3 marks]

10 A cylindrical footstool is 35 cm high with a diameter of 31 cm. Calculate its surface area. Give your answer in cm^2. (Take π = 3.14) [4 marks]

11 Hugo is paid at £9.50/hour in his new job. He works for 35 hours a week. Out of his weekly pay packet, £131 is deducted for taxes. He pays £110 a week in rent for his shared accommodation and needs to contribute £40 a week towards his household bills.

  a Calculate how much Hugo has left per week for living expenses. [4 marks]

  b Hugo is told that his rent will rise by 8% and his bills by 20%. He asks his line manager for an increase in his hourly rate to cover these rises. If he works the same number of hours per week, what increase does he need in his hourly rate to cover the rises? Give your answer to the nearest 10p. [4 marks]

12 Calculate the area of a circle with a diameter of 40 cm. Give your answer in cm^2. (Take π = 3.14) [2 marks]

13 a The price of an electric car increases by 8%. The cost of the car was £32,500. Calculate the increase in the cost of the car. [2 marks]

  b The cost of a sofa normally priced at £840 decreases by 27.5%. Calculate by how much the cost of the sofa has decreased. [2 marks]

14 Harry puts £5,200 in a bank which pays annual compound interest of 3%. Calculate how much interest the money earns after 3 years. [3 marks]

15 The 9 spheres that make up the Atomium in Brussels, Belgium, each have a diameter of 1,800 cm. Calculate the total volume of the 9 spheres (in cubic metres) to the nearest ten cubic metres. [3 marks]

(The formula for the volume of a sphere is $\frac{4}{3}\pi r^3$)

16 The circle shown has diameter 12 m. The shaded area represents a third of the circle. [3 marks] Calculate its area. (Take π = 3.14)

17 Jagjeet is painting a post box. He will not paint the base or the letter box. Calculate the total surface area of the post box. Give your answer correct to one decimal place. [4 marks]

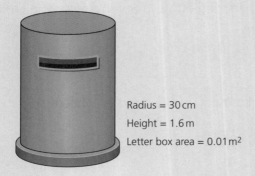

Radius = 30 cm
Height = 1.6 m
Letter box area = 0.01 m²

18 A Malteser chocolate (sphere) has a honeycombed centre with an outer covering of chocolate.

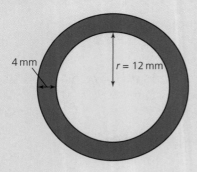

4 mm

$r = 12$ mm

What is the volume of chocolate covering the Malteser? Give your answer to one decimal place. [4 marks]

(The formula for the volume of a sphere is $\frac{4}{3}\pi r^3$. Take $\pi = 3.14$)

19 Arthur drives from village A to village E via villages B, C and D. On the way back to village A, he takes a different route, without passing through villages B, C and D.

He drives back at an average speed of 36 miles per hour and it takes him 45 minutes.
Is his journey back from E to A, a shorter distance than his journey from A to E? [4 marks]

Show your workings. Take 1 mile = 1.6 km.

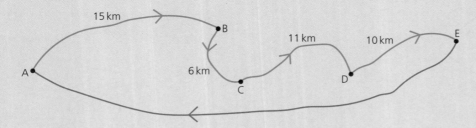

15 km

B

11 km   10 km   E

A   6 km   D

C

20 The diagram below shows a front elevation of a square-based pyramid on top of a cuboid. The ratio of the height (h) of the cuboid to the height (p) of the pyramid is 3 : 2.

If the area of the base of the pyramid is 20.25 cm² and the volume of the cuboid is 121.5 cm³ then calculate the overall height of the composite shape. [3 marks]

p

h

21 A horse, tied to a stationary post by a rope 7 m long, pulls a cart in a circular arc at a speed of 4 km/h. The horse starts the journey north of the post. Calculate the angle (to the nearest degree) the horse will have reached after 9 seconds.   [5 marks]

(Take π = 3.14)

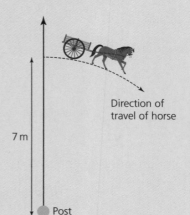

Direction of
travel of horse

7 m

Post

22 A piece of gold with a density 19.32 g/cm^3 is placed into a water tank of length 64.7 cm and width 0.5 m. The water in the tank rises by 2 cm. Calculate the mass of the gold. Give your answer in kilograms.   [4 marks]

23 Using the conversion 1 lb = 0.45 kg, calculate the weight (in pounds) of a man weighing 79 kg. Give your answer to the nearest whole number.   [2 marks]

24 Nadia drives along a road that has a speed limit of 60 miles per hour. It takes her 2 minutes to drive between two average speed cameras, which are 3.4 km apart.

Nadia says that her average speed between the two cameras was not above the speed limit. Is she correct? Show how you get your answer.   [4 marks]

(1 km = 0.625 miles).

25 Look at the 2-D representation of a square-based pyramid. Calculate the surface area of the pyramid.   [3 marks]

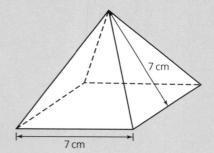

7 cm

7 cm

26 A golf ball has a diameter of 1.7 inches. The dimensions of a shoe box are 10.5 inches long by 7 inches wide by 3.75 inches high. Calculate how many golf balls will fit into the shoe box.   [4 marks]

27 A hungry sheep is tethered at point X in a field as shown in the diagram. The sheep's lead is 5 m long. What is the percentage (to one decimal place) of the field that the sheep can eat from? [5 marks]

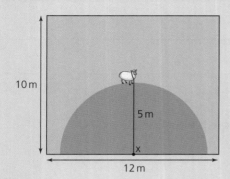

28 A woman is paid at the rate of £15.50/hour for some part-time work. She earns £372 in one week. Calculate how many hours she worked in that week. [2 marks]

29 Look at the 2-D representation of a triangular prism.

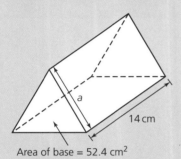

14 cm

Area of base = 52.4 cm²

The total surface area of the prism is 566.8 cm². Calculate the length *a* shown on the diagram of the triangular prism. [5 marks]

30 The radius of this sphere is 3.5 cm. Calculate:

a its volume [3 marks]

b its surface area. [3 marks]

Give both answers to one decimal place.

(Volume of a sphere = $\frac{4}{3}\pi r^3$ and the surface area of a sphere = $4\pi r^2$; $\pi = 3.14$)

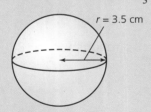

r = 3.5 cm

31 The following diagram represents a garden. New grass is to be placed in the shaded area.

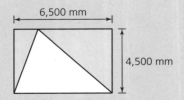

6,500 mm

4,500 mm

Calculate the area of the new grass. [3 marks]

32 A cuboid tank is filled with water. A stone of volume 150 cm³ is dropped into the tank causing the water to rise by 0.4 cm. The length of the tank is 30 cm. Calculate its width (in centimetres). [5 marks]

3 Handling information and data

DIAGNOSTIC QUESTIONS

 Non-calculator questions

1 Last year, Sarah's average (mean) score for her tests in English was 64%.

   This year, her scores are:

   68%   59%   63%   71%   61%   68%

   Has she improved on her results from last year? Give a reason for your answer.

2 The following table shows the temperatures across seven different cities one morning in January:

Swansea	Coventry	London	Glasgow	Newcastle	Norwich	Sheffield
−1°C	0°C	2°C	−7°C	−4°C	4°C	−4°C

   Calculate the temperature:

   a   range   b   median   c   mode.

3 A teacher in a class creates a table to show which of his students have GCSE English. He groups them according to the age ranges 16–17 and 18+.

	16–17 year olds	18+
With GCSE English	7	12
Without GCSE English	9	5

   A student is chosen at random. What is the probability of the student being a 16–17 year old with a GCSE in English?

4 A bag contains red, blue and yellow counters. If one is chosen at random, the probability of it being a red is $\frac{1}{5}$ and the probability of it being blue is 35%. Calculate the probability of the counter being yellow. Give your answer as:

   a   a percentage   b   a decimal   c   a fraction.

5 The scatter diagram below shows the correlation between seven students' results for an IT test and music test:

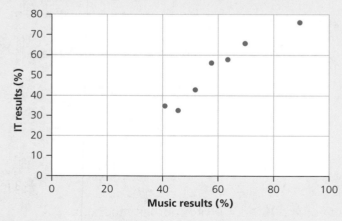

a Draw a line of best fit to show the correlation between the students' IT and music scores.

b Describe the correlation between the students' IT and music results.

c One student scored 80% in their music test, but missed the IT test. Using your line of best fit, estimate what their IT result would have been (show your working on the graph).

Calculator question

6 Debbie recorded the times, in minutes, for 20 students to complete an initial assessment. She recorded her results in the grouped frequency table below:

Time (t) mins	Frequency	
$20 \leq t < 30$	3	$3 \times 25 =$
$30 \leq t < 40$	4	
$40 \leq t < 50$	9	
$50 \leq t < 60$	4	

Estimate the mean time to complete the initial assessment.

3.1 Calculate the median and mode of a set of quantities

The median

The median is a type of average (do not confuse with the mean). It is the **midpoint** of a set of values when they are placed in numerical order (i.e. from lowest to highest).

The median can be a better measure of average than the mean if the data contains extreme values (either very high or very low), known as 'outliers'.

The mode

The mode (or modal value) of a set of quantities is the number that appears the most often.

> **MAKING LINKS**
>
> How to calculate the mean is covered in detail in Level 1, Unit 3.3.

> **Median**: the midpoint value in a data set or list of numbers.
>
> **Mode**: the number that appears most often in a data sample.

WORKED EXAMPLE

The ages of a group of adults in a class are recorded below.

24, 19, 34, 28, 30, 36, 26, 23, 41, 34

a Find the median.

b Find the mode

c Another adult, aged 32, joins the class. Calculate the new median.

ANSWER

a Place the numbers in numerical order: 19, 23, 24, 26, **28**,|**30**, 34, 34, 36, 41.

Count the number of values. There is an **even** number of ages (10), so we can put a line between the two middle numbers (28 and 30). The median value is midway between those two numbers, so it is **29**.

Alternatively, you could add the two middle numbers (28 + 30 = 58) and divide by 2 (**29**) to find the median.

b The mode of the above set of quantities is the number which occurs the most: **34**.

c Now there are 11 numbers (odd). The median value is then the number in the middle, **30**, which has the same amount of numbers (5) on either side of it.

19, 23, 24, 26, 28, **30**, 32, 34, 34, 36, 41

> **EXAM TIP**
>
> Make sure, when rearranging the numbers in ascending order, that all numbers from the data set are included and that the position of the median is indicated clearly.

COMMON MISTAKE

A common mistake here is to calculate the median from the set of numbers before putting them in order. In this case, it would be 33, which is between 30 and 36.

CHECK YOUR UNDERSTANDING

1   Work out the mode and the median of the following weights:
    65.3 kg, 84 kg, 54.0 kg, 82.4 kg, 91 kg, 84.2 kg, 84.0 kg, 76.7 kg,
    88.5 kg

2   The following table shows the temperatures in 10 cities across the
    UK on a January morning:

City	Temperature (°C)	City	Temperature (°C)
Edinburgh	−3	Liverpool	−1
Bristol	5	Norwich	4
London	3	Belfast	−3
Cardiff	6	Aberdeen	−5
Birmingham	0	Sunderland	−2

   a   What is the modal temperature?
   b   Calculate the median temperature.

3   A student measures the lengths of six pieces of wood. She
    calculates that the median value is 2 m. However, when she
    records her results, she leaves out one of the measurements.
    Calculate the missing measurement.
    1.4 m, 2.3 m, 0.9 m, 3.2 m, 1.8 m, ?

3.2 Estimate the mean of a grouped frequency distribution from discrete data

The mean

The mean of a data set is the total sum of all the numbers in that data set, divided by the number of values in the set.

A grouped frequency distribution is where discrete data is grouped together in **intervals** and placed in a table, called a frequency table.

The frequency column in a table is the number of things in each interval. In a grouped frequency distribution, the following symbols are used:

- < means less than
- ≤ means less than or equal to
- > means greater than
- ≥ means greater than or equal to

> **Mean:** a type of average; the values are added and the total divided by the amount of values.
>
> **Discrete data:** data with specific values, e.g. shoe size or the number of students in a class.

WORKED EXAMPLE

A teacher has 30 adults in her class. She records their ages in a grouped frequency table:

Age (a) of adults in class	Frequency
$18 \leq a < 24$	5
$24 \leq a < 30$	10
$30 \leq a < 36$	8
$36 \leq a < 42$	3
$42 \leq a < 48$	4

Estimate the mean age of the adult students in her class.

> **EXAM TIP**
>
> The mid-point of each interval is taken as the best estimate for the ages of the adults in that interval.

ANSWER

The first line in the table shows that five adults have an age greater than or equal to 18 ($18 \leq a$), but less than 24 ($a < 24$).

For each group interval (e.g. $18 \leq a < 24$), take the mid-point of that interval (here, 21) and multiply it by the number of adults ($21 \times 5 = 105$).

Age (a) of adults in class	Frequency	Mid-point × frequency	Estimated totals
$18 \leq a < 24$	5	21×5	105
$24 \leq a < 30$	10	27×10	270
$30 \leq a < 36$	8	33×8	264
$36 \leq a < 42$	3	39×3	117
$42 \leq a < 48$	4	45×4	180
	30		**936**

To get the total (estimated) age of the 30 adults, add up the estimated totals for each group interval (the numbers in the right-hand column): 936

To find an estimate for the mean age, divide the total (estimated) age by the number of adults:

$$\text{estimated mean age} = \frac{\text{total (estimated) age}}{\text{number of adults}} = \frac{936}{30}$$

$$= \underset{30 \overline{)93^33^36.^60}}{\overset{3\ 1.\ 2}{}}$$

estimated mean age = **31.2 years**

CHECK YOUR UNDERSTANDING

1 A student recorded the mass (in kg) of 12 different dogs and placed their results in a grouped frequency table.
Calculate an estimate for the mean mass of the dogs.

Mass (m) in kg	Frequency
$0 < m \le 10$	2
$10 < m \le 20$	3
$20 < m \le 30$	4
$30 < m \le 40$	2
$40 < m \le 50$	1

2 A teacher asks their students how long they spend on their phones every day during their holiday. The frequency table shows the results:

Time spent (t) in hours	Frequency
$0 \le t < 1$	4
$1 \le t < 2$	6
$2 \le t < 3$	7
$3 \le t < 4$	6
$4 \le t < 5$	4

Estimate the mean time (in hours) that the students spend on their phones every day during their holiday.

3 A member of a scrabble club records the scores of the members after a game. The following data represents the results:

Score (s)	Frequency
$140 \le s < 150$	2
$150 \le s < 160$	4
$160 \le s < 170$	4
$170 \le s < 180$	3
$180 \le s < 190$	2

Estimate the mean score of the members of the scrabble club.
Give your answer to 1 decimal place.

3.3 Use the mean, median, mode and range to compare two sets of data

REVISED

Mean, median, mode and range

The mean, median, mode and range can be used to compare two sets of data. Questions comparing two sets of data involve calculating a value in one set of data (e.g. mean or median), and comparing it with the same value in the other set of data.

> **Range:** the difference between the largest and smallest values in a data set.

MAKING LINKS

How to calculate the mean and range is covered in Level 1, Section 3.4. How to calculate the median and mode is in Section 3.1, page 84.

WORKED EXAMPLE

Paulo records the heights of a group of eight students in his class (group A):

  1.64 m, 1.64 m, 1.70 m, 1.76 m, 1.82 m, 1.83 m, 1.72 m, 1.84 m

He then records the heights of another eight students in his class (group B). The median height is 1.77 m. Write a statement comparing the two median values.

> **ANSWER**
>
> Calculate the median of the eight students in group A. Place the values in numerical order:
>
>   1.64 m, 1.64 m, 1.70 m, <u>1.72 m</u> | <u>1.76 m</u>, 1.82 m, 1.83 m, 1.84 m
>
> The median is midway between the two middle numbers (1.72 m and 1.76 m) = **1.74 m**
>
> Write a statement making the comparison.
>
> **The median height for group B (1.77 m) is higher than the median height for group A (1.74 m).**

COMMON MISTAKE

A common mistake here would be to forget to place the numbers in numerical order so calculating the median as 1.76 m | 1.82 m = **1.79 m** in error.

EXAM TIP

When writing a statement to compare values keep it short and clear. It's often just saying that one value is higher (or lower) than another.

WORKED EXAMPLE

A student wants to know if it takes him longer to cycle to college or walk to college.

He records the time it takes over five journeys by cycle and five journeys by foot in the table below.

Time to cycle to college (mins)	24	22	24	26	28
Time to walk to college (mins)	25	26	23	23	24

  a Write a statement comparing the mean times it takes him over the five journeys.

  b Which of the times were most consistent, cycling to college or walking to college? Give a reason for your answer.

EXAM TIP

When comparing two sets of data to find the most consistent, the examiner is looking for the two ranges to be compared. The set of data with the lower range will be the more consistent (its values will vary less).

ANSWER

a First, add the minutes up for the five journeys for cycling and walking. Then calculate the means for cycling and walking.

$$\text{mean time to cycle} = \frac{\text{total time}}{\text{number of journeys}} = \frac{124}{5} = 5\overline{)12\,^24.\,^40} \quad \begin{array}{c} 2\ 4\ .\ 8 \end{array} = \textbf{24.8 mins}$$

$$\text{mean time to walk} = \frac{\text{total time}}{\text{number of journeys}} = \frac{121}{5} = 5\overline{)12\,^21.\,^10} \quad \begin{array}{c} 2\ 4\ .\ 2 \end{array} = \textbf{24.2 mins}$$

The mean time to walk to college (24.2 mins) was shorter than the mean time to cycle to college (24.8 mins).

b Range of cycle times = 28 − 22 = 6 mins
Range of walk times = 26 − 23 = 3 mins

The walk times were more consistent, as they varied the least (had a smaller range).

CHECK YOUR UNDERSTANDING

1 Compare the modal values of the following sets of data provided by two groups of students:

Group A	58 L	63 L	61 L	75 L	72 L	53 L	63 L	74 L	59 L
Group B	58 L	62 L	74 L	65 L	75 L	64 L	60 L	74 L	69 L

2 Zubeida records her profit over the first 5 months of the year on a line graph. Her mean (average) profit over the same 5-month period the previous year was £115,000.
Write a statement comparing the two means.

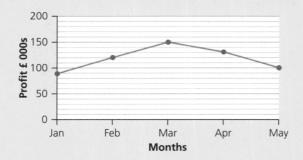

3 Aman measures and records the heights of a group of eight plants:

458 mm   482 mm   0.396 m   42.8 cm
46.2 cm   470 mm   460 mm   0.465 m

He then records the heights of a second group of plants. The median height of this group is 46.5 cm. Write a statement comparing the median values of the two groups of plants.

EXAM TIP

When you have values with different units (e.g. mm, cm and m), change them all to the same unit to make them easier to compare and organise.

3.4 Express probabilities as fractions, decimals and percentages

The **probability** of an event occurring is a measure of how likely it is that event will happen. It is calculated by dividing the number of possibilities of the event happening by the total number of possible outcomes.

> **Probability:** the measure of how likely an event is to occur.

The probability of an event occurring can be expressed as a fraction, decimal or percentage.

WORKED EXAMPLE

48 counters are used in a game: 12 red, 12 blue, 12 green and 12 yellow. One is picked at random. What is the probability that:

a   It will be a blue?

b   It will not be red.

Express each answer as a fraction, decimal and percentage.

> **ANSWER**
>
> a   There are 12 blue counters and 48 counters in total. So, the probability of picking a blue counter is 12 out of 48 or $\frac{12}{48}$.
> This can be simplified to $\frac{1}{4}$ and expressed as a decimal **(0.25)** or a percentage **(25%)**.
>
> b   There are 36 counters that are not red. So, the probability of picking a counter that is not red is 36 out of 48 or $\frac{36}{48}$.
> This can be simplified to $\frac{3}{4}$ and expressed as a decimal **(0.75)** or a percentage **(75%)**.

> **MAKING LINKS**
>
> Identifying and knowing the equivalence between fractions, decimals and percentages is covered in Section 1.4, page 15.

CHECK YOUR UNDERSTANDING

1   In a class of boys and girls, the probability of a girl being chosen at random by the teacher is 0.425. Calculate the probability, as a fraction, of a boy being chosen at random.

2   The probability of a team winning a football match is two fifths. The probability that they draw is three eighths. What is the probability that the team loses? Give your answer:

   a   as a fraction

   b   as a percentage

   c   as a decimal.

3   There are sixty coloured counters in a bag. One of the counters is red, and two of the counters are blue. If one of the counters is picked from the bag at random, what is the probability that it will be a counter other than a red or a blue? Give your answer:

   a   as a percentage

   b   as a decimal.

3.5 Work out the probability of combined events including the use of diagrams and tables, including two-way tables

Combined events

The probability of combined events looks at what the probability of two events occurring **independently** of each other. If an event occurs independently of another it does not affect the probability of the other event occurring.

The probability of combined events can be represented in diagrams (e.g. a tree diagram) and tables (e.g. a two-way table).

> **WORKED EXAMPLE**
>
>
>
> What is the probability of flipping a coin and it landing on tails, and then rolling a die and it landing on a 4?
>
> > **ANSWER**
> >
> > These are **independent** events – flipping a coin does not affect the number scored when you roll a die.
> >
> > When you flip a coin, there are two possible outcomes: heads or tails. If you roll a die, there are six possible outcomes: 1, 2, 3, 4, 5 or 6.
> >
> > Write out all the possible outcomes in a table or list:
> >
> > | Die shows | H | T |
> > |---|---|---|
> > | 1 | 1H | 1T |
> > | 2 | 2H | 2T |
> > | 3 | 3H | 3T |
> > | 4 | 4H | **4T** |
> > | 5 | 5H | 5T |
> > | 6 | 6H | 6T |
> >
> > 1H, 1T, 2H, 2T, 3H, 3T, 4H, 4T, 5H, 5T, 6H, 6T
> >
> > From the table and list there are 12 possible outcomes.
> >
> > So, the probability of the **coin landing on a tail** and the **die landing on a 4**, is 1 in 12, which can be expressed as $\frac{1}{12}$.
> >
> > Alternatively, you can multiply the probability of getting a tail by the probability of getting a 4.
> >
> > $$\frac{1}{2} \times \frac{1}{6} = \frac{1}{12}$$

EXAM TIP

When multiplying fractions, multiply the numerators (1 × 1 = 1) and the denominators (2 × 6 = 12).

> **COMMON MISTAKES**
>
> Common mistakes here include leaving the probability as one outcome (e.g. $\frac{1}{6}$ instead of $\frac{1}{12}$) or adding the two probabilities rather than multiplying them.

Two-way tables

The probability of a combined event can also be calculated from data given in a two-way table.

> Two-way table: a table that shows the frequencies for two variables, with one being represented using rows and the other using columns.

WORKED EXAMPLE

John sells T-shirts to raise money for a charity event. The two-way table shows the two sizes of T-shirts he is selling and how many have a logo.

	Small	Large
With a logo	15	12
Without a logo	18	16

a John picks one of the T-shirts at random. What is the probability the T-shirt is small and without a logo?

b John picks a large T-shirt. What is the probability of the T-shirt being without a logo?

ANSWER

a From the table, the number of T-shirts that are small and without a logo is 18.
We then need to calculate the total number of T-shirts.
The number of small T-shirts = 15 + 18 = 33.
The number of large T-shirts = 12 + 16 = 28.
So, the total number of T-shirts = 33 + 28 = 61.
Or,
The number of T-shirts with a logo = 15 + 12 = 27.
The number of T-shirts without a logo = 18 + 16 = 34.
So, the total number of T-shirts = 27 + 34 = 61.
So, the probability of the T-shirt being small and without a logo is 18 out of 61 = $\frac{18}{61}$.

b From the table, the number of large T-shirts without a logo = 16.
The total number of large T-shirts is 28.
So, the probability of the large T-shirt being without a logo is $\frac{16}{28}$ or $\frac{4}{7}$.

COMMON MISTAKES

A common mistake in part **a** is to base the probability on just one row $\left(\frac{18}{33}\right)$ or one column $\left(\frac{18}{34}\right)$, rather than the total number $\left(\frac{18}{63}\right)$. A common mistake in part b, on the other hand, is to base the probability on the total $\left(\frac{16}{63}\right)$ rather than on just one column $\left(\frac{16}{28}\right)$.

Tree diagrams

A **tree diagram** (or probability tree) clearly records all the possible outcomes of an event. It helps to calculate the number of possible outcomes. In a tree diagram, all the probabilities in a branch add up to one.

> Tree diagram: a clear way of recording all the possible outcomes of an event.

WORKED EXAMPLE

The tree diagram shows the probability of adults in a class reading a daily newspaper.

a Complete the diagram.

b One of the students in the class is chosen at random. What is the probability of that student being a male who does not read a newspaper?

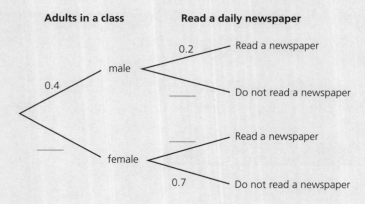

ANSWER

a The diagram shows that the proportion of males in the class is 0.4 (or 40% or $\frac{2}{5}$).

Therefore, the proportion of females will be $1 - 0.4 = $ **0.6** (or 60% or $\frac{3}{5}$).

The diagram also shows that the proportion of males in the class that read a newspaper $= 0.2$ (or 20% or $\frac{1}{5}$). Therefore, the proportion of males in the class that do not read a newspaper will be $1 - 0.2 = $ **0.8** (or 80% or $\frac{4}{5}$), since all the possible outcomes of an event occurring add up to one.

Similarly, the proportion of females that read a newspaper will be $1 - 0.7 = $ **0.3** (or 30% or $\frac{3}{10}$).

The probability tree diagram can now be completed:

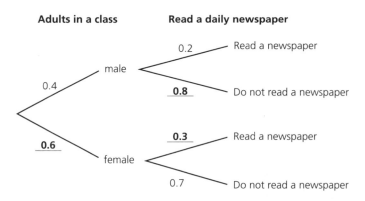

b The probability of the student being a male is 0.4 and the probability of a male not reading a newspaper is 0.8.

The probability of the student being a male who does not read a newspaper is $0.4 \times 0.8 = $ **0.32**.

1   Two **fair** spinners are spun.

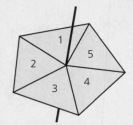 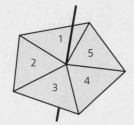

> Fair: in probability, this means that all outcomes are equally likely to occur.

   a   What is the probability that both spinners will land on a 4?

   b   Complete the following table to show all the possible outcomes for the total score of the two spinners being spun:

	1	2	3	4	5
1					
2					
3					
4					
5					

   c   What is the probability of the total score being 9?

   d   What is the probability of the total score being 5 or 6?

2   A survey is carried out into whether pets are allowed into different types of café. The results are recorded in the following two-way table:

	Non-vegetarian cafe	Vegetarian café	Vegan café
Pets allowed	13	14	17
Pets not allowed	12	8	7

   a   One of the cafés that took part in the survey is chosen at random. What is the probability that this café will be a vegetarian café where pets are not allowed?

   b   Another café is chosen at random. What is the probability that this café will be one where pets are allowed?

3   Dania throws two fair dice.
    The numbers on dice A are: 3, −2, 2, −1, 1, 0.
    The numbers on dice B are: −3, 2, −2, 1, −1, 0.
    The table shows some total scores from throwing the two dice.

	3	−2	2	−1	1	0
−3	0		−1		−2	
2	5					
−2		−4		−1		
1	4		3	0		
−1		−3		−2		−1
0	3		2		1	

   a   Complete the table.

   b   Dania throws the two dice once. What is the probability that the total score is 0?

   c   Dania throws the two dice again. What is the probability that the new total score will be −2?

3.6 Draw and interpret scatter diagrams and recognise positive and negative correlation

> Correlation: describes the relationship between variables. It can be positive or negative.

A scatter diagram can show the correlation (relationship) between two variables. For example, temperature and the sale of sunscreen (left) or number of local supermarkets and the distance from the town centre (right).

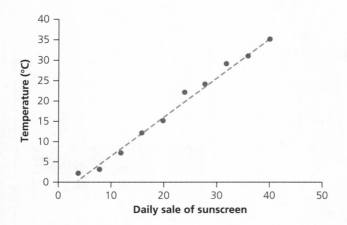

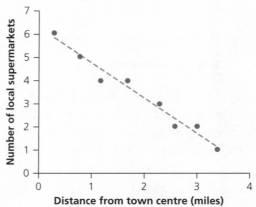

The correlation between temperature and sale of sunscreen (left) is a positive correlation. As the temperature **increases**, the daily sale of sunscreen **increases**.

The correlation between the number of local supermarkets and the distance from the town centre (right) is a negative correlation. The number of supermarkets **decreases** as the distance from the town centre **increases**.

Correlation can be represented by a line of best fit (or a 'trend line'). A line of best fit passes through the data points with roughly the same number on either side of the line and best represents those points.

> Positive correlation: a relationship when two variables move in the same direction, i.e. one variable increases as the other increases or one variable decreases as the other decreases.
>
> Negative correlation: a relationship when two variables move in different directions, i.e. one variable increases while the other decreases.
>
> Line of best fit: a straight line that passes centrally through the points on a scatter graph and best represents those points.

WORKED EXAMPLE

A teacher wants to see if there is a correlation between the amount of time his students spend on their smartphones at the weekend and the amount of time they spend reading.

He records his results in a scatter diagram:

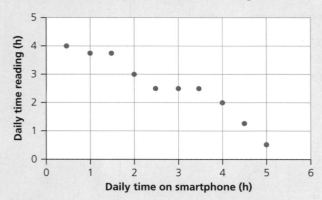

He leaves out results from two of his students.

a   Add the following two students to the scatter graph:
Charity: 3 hours on the phone and 2 hours reading.
Miguel: 4½ hours on the phone and 1 hour 45 mins reading.

b   Draw a line of best fit for the data.

c   Describe the correlation between the amount of time students spend on their smartphones at the weekend and the amount of time they spend reading.

d   Another student states that they spend one and a half hours reading at the weekend. Estimate how much time they spend on their smartphone.

ANSWER

a   The two extra students have been added to the scatter diagram, indicated with crosses.

b

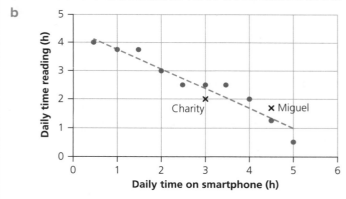

c   The line of best fit shows that as the amount of time students spend on their smartphones increases, the amount of time they spend on reading goes down. Therefore, there is a negative correlation between the two.

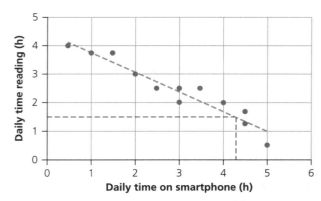

d   Use the line of best fit that you drew to estimate how much time the student spends on their phone.

At $1\frac{1}{2}$ hours on the vertical axis (1.5 hours) draw a horizontal line across to the line of best fit. Where your line meets the line of best fit, draw a vertical line down to horizontal axis. It cuts the axis at about 4 hours 18 mins.

So, the estimated time the student spends on their smartphone is 4 hours and 18 minutes.

CHECK YOUR UNDERSTANDING

1   The scatter graph shows plant growth in mm against daily hours of sunshine.
   a   Draw a line of best fit on the graph.
   b   Describe the correlation the graph shows.

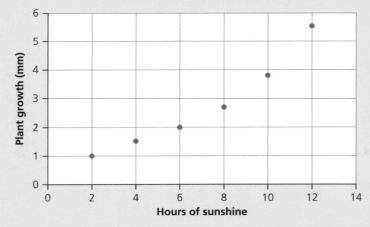

2 The scatter diagram shows the number of gym memberships sold in the first few weeks of 2022.

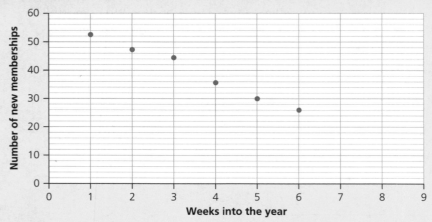

a   In week seven, 22 new memberships were sold and in week eight there were 15 new memberships. Plot these extra points on the scatter graph.

b   Draw a line of best fit on the scatter graph.

c   Describe the correlation between the number of new gym memberships and weeks of the year.

3 The scatter graph shows data about the mass (in kg) and length (in cm) of 8 mountain goats.

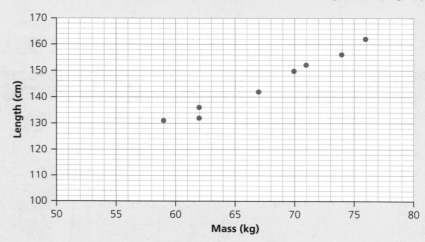

a   The mass and length of another three mountain goats is recorded in the table below. Add this data to the scatter graph above.

Length (cm)	Mass (kg)
144	65
138	65
149	68

b   Draw a line of best fit on the scatter graph

c   Describe the correlation between the mountain goats' mass and lengths.

d   Another mountain goat's length is measured as 156 cm. Using the line of best fit, estimate their weight.

EXAM-STYLE QUESTIONS

Paper 1 Non-calculator questions

1 Calculate the median of the following set of data. [2 marks]

18.30 m   21.56 m   19.98 m   17.29 m   21.65 m   19.42 m

2 A group of students did a survey in their local town centre. They asked people at random if they worked full-time and, if so, what their annual salary was. They recorded their results in the table below:

Person	Annual salary (£)	Person	Annual salary (£)
1	25,000	5	29,000
2	15,600	6	19,000
3	21,000	7	100,000
4	12,000	8	32,000

The students want to work out an average annual salary from their results. What do you think would give a better result, the mean or the median? Explain your answer. [1 mark]

3 The following table shows the temperatures in eight towns and cities across the UK on a February morning:

City	Temp (°C)	City	Temp (°C)
Glasgow	−3	Manchester	−1
Torquay	6	Inverness	−5
London	3	Ballycastle	−3
Luton	4	Canterbury	5

Abdul calculates the range as 6°C − 5°C = 1°C. Is he correct? Explain your answer. [1 mark]

4 There are a mix of green, red and blue balls in a bag. The chance of picking a green one at random is 0.41 and that of picking a red one is 0.43.

Calculate the chance, as a fraction in its simplest form, of a blue ball being picked at random. [3 marks]

5 A family are researching hotel weekend breaks online. They want to know if breakfast is included in the price of the hotel and if the hotels have an indoor swimming pool.

They record their findings in the following two-way table:

	Breakfast included	Breakfast not included
Indoor swimming pool	9	8
No swimming pool	13	10

They choose one of the hotels at random.

a What is the probability that this hotel has breakfast included and has an indoor swimming pool? Give your answer as:

    i a fraction [2 marks]

    ii a percentage [2 marks]

    iii a decimal. [1 mark]

b The family decide to choose another hotel. What is the probability that this hotel will be one where breakfast is not included? [2 marks]

6 The 54 cards in a pack include four suits - 13 hearts, 13 spades, 13 diamonds and 13 clubs - and 2 jokers. The hearts and diamonds are red cards, and the clubs and spades are black cards. If a card is picked at random, what is the probability that:

    a   The card will be a joker?   [2 marks]

    b   The card will be a red?   [2 marks]

    c   The card will be a club?   [2 marks]

    d   The card will not be a heart?   [2 marks]

7 The scatter graph shows the relationship between the number of staff working in a call centre against call waiting time (in minutes) for customers.

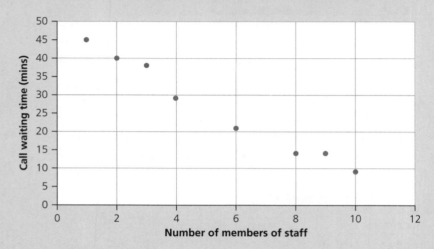

The table below shows data for two missing results:

Number of members of staff	Call waiting time
7	15
11	7

    a   Add the missing data to the scatter graph.   [2 marks]

    b   Draw a line of best fit on the scatter graph.   [1 mark]

    c   Describe the correlation between the number of staff working at the call centre and call waiting times for customers.   [1 mark]

    d   The call waiting time for five members of staff is missing from the scatter graph. Using the line of best fit, estimate the call waiting time for customers.   [1 mark]

8 Six students recorded their spending over one weekend:

£37.75, £24.50, £51.29, £65, £54.70, £18

Calculate their median spend.   [3 marks]

9   The person who lives in Holly Bush Cottage, Sleigh Bell Lane, has made a lucky
    dip for any carol singers who knock at their door.

    The lucky dip contains one pound coin, two 50p coins, three 10p coins, two
    chocolate truffles and four mince pies. What is the probability that the first singer:

    a   will pick some money?   [1 mark]
    b   will pick a 50p coin?   [1 mark]
    c   will pick a mince pie?   [1 mark]
    d   will pick a chocolate truffle?   [1 mark]
    e   will pick some food?   [1 mark]
    f   will pick something other than a 10p coin?   [1 mark]

    The first singer picks the pound coin. What is the probability that the second singer:

    g   will pick some money?   [1 mark]
    h   will pick a 50p coin?   [1 mark]
    i   will pick a mince pie?   [1 mark]

    The second singer picks a 10p coin. What is the probability that the third singer:

    j   will pick some food?   [1 mark]
    k   will pick some money?   [1 mark]
    l   will pick a 10p coin?   [1 mark]
    m   will pick a pound coin?   [1 mark]

10 Callum has 200 packets of crisps in a box. The flavours are salt and vinegar, ready
    salted, cheese and onion, and prawn cocktail. If he picks one of the packets at
    random, the probability of picking a packet of prawn cocktail crisps is 1 in 8.

    Twenty percent of the packets are cheese and onion, and two fifths of the packets
    are salt and vinegar. Calculate how many packets of ready salted crisps are in the box.   [4 marks]

11 The following table shows the probability of snow across five days in winter:

Day	Mon	Tues	Wed	Thurs	Fri
Probability of snow	0.3	35%	20%	0.375	20%

    Calculate the probability that there will be snow on Wednesday and Thursday.
    Give your answer as a fraction.   [3 marks]

Paper 2 Calculator questions

1   A fitness instructor records the time it takes the adults in her morning class to complete
    an exercise.

    She puts the results in the following table:

Time (secs)	24.9	18.6	25	25.1	21.9	22.4	22.4

    She also records the times taken for the adults in her afternoon class to complete the same
    exercise. For the afternoon group, the average (mean) time is 23.3 and the range of results is 9.5.

    a   Write a statement comparing the average (mean) time for the adults to complete
        the exercise of the morning and afternoon classes.   [4 marks]
    b   In which class are the results more consistent? Give a reason for your answer.   [2 marks]

2 The chart shows the temperature change over a week in a city. The upper values show the maximum temperature each day and the lower values show the minimum values each day.

	Fri 6	Sat 7	Sun 8	Mon 9	Tue 10	Wed 11	Thu 12
Max	25°	28°	29°	24°	24°	24°	24°
Min	18°	18°	18°	17°	17°	18°	17°

    a What is the modal maximum temperature? [1 mark]

    b What is the median maximum temperature? [2 marks]

    c What is the modal minimum temperature? [1 mark]

    d What is the median minimum temperature? [2 marks]

3 Triangular, square, rectangular and circular plastic shapes are placed in a box. The ratio of the shapes is 4 : 3 : 5 : 14. A shape is picked from the box at random.

Calculate the probability that the shape will have more than one right angle. Give your answer as:

    a a fraction [2 marks]

    b a decimal (to three decimal places) [2 marks]

    c a percentage (to one decimal place). [2 marks]

4 Two fair dice are thrown at the same time. Select the probability of scoring a total of 7. [1 mark]

    A 16.7%

    B 0.27

    C 17.7%

    D $\frac{7}{36}$

5 Sumina plays football for her local team on Saturdays and Sundays. The probability tree diagram shows the probability of Sumina scoring in a game on Saturday and a game on Sunday.

    a Complete the probability tree diagram. [2 marks]

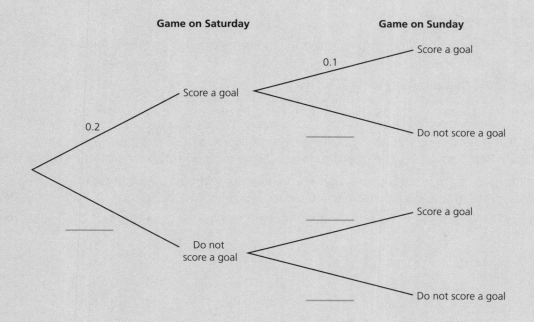

b Work out the probability that Sumina will not score a goal on either Saturday or Sunday. Give your answer as a:

    i decimal   [2 marks]

    ii percentage   [1 mark]

    iii fraction in its simplest form.   [2 marks]

6 A survey asks adult students in a college if they study English and maths in addition to their main programme. The results are put in the table below:

Subject	English only	Maths only	English and maths	Neither English nor maths
Number of adults	34	43	35	29

One of the students is chosen at random. What is the probability of that student studying maths only? Give your answer as:

a a fraction   [2 marks]

b a decimal (to three decimal places)   [2 marks]

c a percentage (to one decimal place).   [1 mark]

7 A student sees this sign (made from tiles) on their classroom wall:

YOU MUST SHOW YOUR WORKINGS CLEARLY

a The student picks one of the letters at random. What is the probability that the letter will be an O? Give your answer as:

    i a fraction (in its simplest form)   [2 marks]

    ii a decimal (to three decimal places)   [2 marks]

    iii a percentage (to one decimal place).   [1 mark]

b The student puts the letter back. They missed some of the words from the sign. It reads in full:

YOU MUST SHOW YOUR WORKINGS CLEARLY AS MARKS ARE AWARDED FOR WORKINGS

The student picks one letter at random. What is the probability that the letter will be an R? Give your answer as:

    i a fraction (in its simplest form)   [2 marks]

    ii a decimal (to two decimal places)   [2 marks]

    iii a percentage (to the nearest whole number).   [1 mark]

8 A cake shop owner has the following cakes on display:

Type of cake	Victoria sponge	Carrot	Red velvet	Lemon drizzle	Date and walnut
Number of cakes	9	13	12	17	6

A customer enters the shop and picks a cake at random. What is the probability that the cake chosen will be a red velvet. Give your answer as:

a a fraction (in its simplest form)   [2 marks]

b a decimal (to two decimal places)   [2 marks]

c a percentage (to the nearest whole number).   [1 mark]

9   Roberto carries out a survey to find out how long his classmates take to get to college each morning. The times and results are recorded in this frequency table.

Time (t) minutes	Frequency
$0 < t \leq 8$	4
$8 < t \leq 16$	6
$16 < t \leq 24$	6
$24 < t \leq 32$	3
$32 < t \leq 40$	1

Calculate an estimate for the mean time it takes for the students in his class to get to college. Give your answer in minutes and seconds. [4 marks]

10 The bar chart shows the ages of football players in an England under-21 team squad. The average (mean) age of football players in the Scottish under-21 team squad is 19.3 years.

Which team has the highest average (mean) age? Give a reason for your answer. [4 marks]

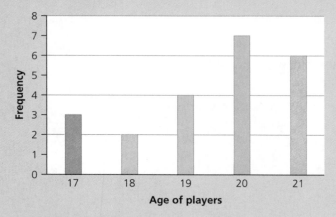

11 The following data represents the heights of 15 adults:

1.60 m	1.78 m	1.59 m	1.80 m	1.48 m
1.80 m	1.88 m	1.73 m	1.50 m	1.55 m
1.81 m	1.65 m	1.69 m	1.82 m	1.83 m

a   Complete the following grouped frequency table: [2 marks]

Interval	Tally	Frequency
$1.4m \leq h < 1.5m$		
$1.5m \leq h < 1.6m$		
$1.6m \leq h < 1.7m$		
$1.7m \leq h < 1.8m$		
$1.8m \leq h < 1.9m$		

b   Estimate the mean height of the 15 adults. [4 marks]

Answers to Diagnostic questions

If you need more guidance on how to calculate the answer or you did not calculate the correct answer, see below each answer for where to look in the book to revise that learning objective.

1 Using numbers and the number system

1 a $\frac{65}{7}$

   b $11\frac{7}{12}$

   c $5\frac{7}{15}$

   d $\frac{11}{12}$

   See Section 1.7 for more on how to order, add, subtract and compare amounts or quantities using proper and improper fractions and mixed numbers.

2 −0.982, −0.908, 0.92, 0.928, 0.98

   See Section 1.9 for more on using decimals when solving problems.

3 $\frac{3}{7}$

   See Section 1.8 for more on using fractions to evaluate one number as a fraction of another.

4 1,214,608

   See Section 1.1 for more on reading, writing, ordering and comparing positive and negative numbers of any size.

5 a $\frac{3}{8}$

   b 37.5%

   c 0.375

   See Section 1.4 for more on identifying and knowing the equivalence between fractions, decimals and percentages.

6 a 125 g

   b 75 mL

   c 0.5 kg

   d 3 (baking trays needed).

   See Section 1.11 for more on understanding and calculating using ratios, direct proportion and inverse proportion.

7 a 1519

   b 50 × 30 = 1500

   See Section 1.2 for more on carrying out calculations with numbers up to one million, including strategies to check answers, including estimation and approximation.

   c 3

   See Section 1.12 for more on following the order of precedence of operators including indices.

8 a 0.3894

   b 2.55

   See Section 1.10 for more on multiplying and dividing (and adding and subtracting) decimals up to three decimal places.

9 £192.50

   See Section 1.3 for more on evaluating expressions and making substitutions in given formulae in words and symbols.

10 £22.31

   See Section 1.5 for more on working out percentages of amounts and expressing one amount as a percentage of another.

11 41.4%

   See Section 1.6 for more on calculating percentage change (any size increase and decrease) and the original value after percentage change.

2 Using common measures, shape and space

1 a 18 cm

   b 14 cm²

   See Section 2.4 for more on calculating perimeters and areas of 2-D shapes (including triangles, circles and composite shapes).

2 2 km

   See Section 2.6 for more on calculating the actual dimensions from scale drawings and creating scale diagrams from given measurements.

3

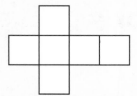

See Section 2.8 for more on understanding and using common 2-D representations of 3-D objects, including drawing nets.

4

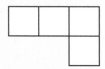

See Section 2.9 for more on how to draw shapes from their plan and elevation view.

5 76

See Section 2.10 for more on calculating the values of angles in different shapes.

6 2.25 miles

See Section 2.3 for more on calculating using compound measures – including speed, density and rates of pay.

7

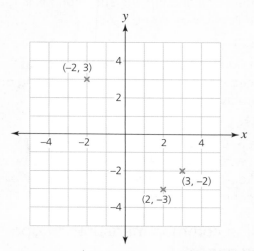

See Section 2.7 for more on using coordinates in 2-D (positive and negative) to specify the positions of points.

8 a 62.8 cm³

b 87.92 cm²

See Section 2.5 for more on using formulae to find the volumes and surface areas of 3-D shapes.

9 1.1 imperial gallons

See Section 2.2 for more on how to calculate between metric and imperial units (including using conversion factors and conversion graphs).

10 £108.80

See Section 2.1 for more on how to calculate discounts (as well as compound interest, percentage increases and decreases).

3 Handling information and data

1 Yes, her results have improved as this year's mean average score is 65%, which is better than the previous year's average of 64%.

See Section 3.3 for more on using the mean, median, mode or range to compare two sets of data.

2 a 11°C

b −1°C

c −4°C

See Section 3.1 for more on how to calculate the median and mode of a set of quantities. Also see Section 3.3 for how to calculate the range.

3 $\frac{7}{33}$

See Section 3.5 for more on working out the probability of combined events, including using two-way tables.

4 a 45%

b 0.45

c $\frac{9}{20}$

See Section 3.4 for more on using probability to assess the likelihood of an outcome.

5 **a** Line of best fit shown here:

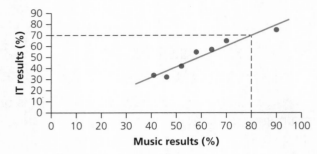

Music results (%)

b There is a positive correlation.

c 70% (shown by drawing a line from the
x-axis at 80% up to the line of best fit and
across to the y-axis which is at 70%).

See Section 3.6 for more on drawing scatter
diagrams, recognising correlation (positive
and negative) and for drawing trend lines.

6

Time (t) mins	Frequency	
$20 \leq t < 30$	3	$3 \times 25 = 75$
$30 \leq t < 40$	4	$4 \times 35 = 140$
$40 \leq t < 50$	9	$9 \times 45 = 405$
$50 \leq t < 60$	4	$4 \times 55 = 220$
	20	840

Estimated mean = 42 mins
See Section 3.2 for more on estimating the mean
of a grouped frequency distribution from discrete
data.

Glossary

Approximation (rounding): finding a value that is close to the correct answer but not exactly equal to it.

Area: a measure of the space inside a 2-D shape.

BIDMAS: an acronym for the correct order of operations in calculations.

Circumference: the total distance around a circle.

Composite shape: a 2-D shape made from a combination of other 2-D shapes.

Compound interest: interest earned on an amount that already has interest added.

Compound measure: a measure that has more than one quantity, e.g. speed, density or rate of pay.

Coordinate: two numbers (x and y) that specify the position of a point on a grid.

Correlation: describes the relationship between variables. It can be positive or negative.

Denominator: the bottom number in a fraction, how many equal parts the whole has been divided into.

Diameter: a straight line from any point on the circumference through the centre (O) to the opposite end of the circumference.

Direct proportion: when the increase (or decrease) in one quantity causes another quantity to increase (or decrease) in the same ratio.

Discrete data: data with specific values, e.g. shoe size or the number of students in a class.

Equivalence: two or more numbers or quantities that are the same.

Equivalent fraction: fractions that represent the same value, but with different numerators and denominators.

Estimation: a rough calculation to find a value.

Expression: a sentence with a minimum of two numbers or variables and at least one mathematical operation.

Fair: in probability, this means that all outcomes are equally likely to occur.

Formula: a mathematical rule, stated in words or mathematical symbols, for working out a value or an amount.

Front elevation: a 2-D drawing of a 3-D shape as seen from the front of the shape.

Improper fraction: a fraction in which the numerator is greater than the denominator.

Indices: shows how many times a number has to be multiplied by itself (also referred to as a power).

Inverse proportion: when the increase (or decrease) in one quantity causes another quantity to decrease (or increase) in the same ratio.

Line of best fit: a straight line that passes centrally through the points on a scatter graph and best represents those points.

Lowest common denominator: the smallest number that can be divided exactly by all the denominators in a group of two or more fractions.

Mean: a type of average; the values are added and the total divided by the amount of values.

Median: the midpoint value in a data set or list of numbers.

Mixed number: a number consisting of an integer and a proper fraction.

Mode: the number that appears most often in a data sample.

Multiple: a number you get when you multiply a given number by an integer. For example, multiples of 6 are 12, 18, 24, 30 etc.

Negative correlation: a relationship when two variables move in different directions, i.e. one variable increases while the other decreases.

Net: what a 3-D object would look like if it was opened out and laid out flat.

Numerator: the top number in a fraction, shows how many of the equal parts there are.

Percentage change: the difference (or change) between two amounts, divided by the original amount, then multiplied by 100%.

Perimeter: the distance around a shape.

Pi: a mathematical constant; the ratio of a circle's circumference to its diameter (approximately 3.14).

Plan view: a 2-D drawing of a 3-D shape as seen from above the shape.

Positive correlation: a relationship when two variables move in the same direction, e.g., one variable increases as the other increases or one variable decreases as the other decreases.

Probability: the measure of how likely an event is to occur.

Proper fraction: a fraction that is less than one, with the numerator less than the denominator.

Proportion: the quantity, size or number of one thing or group as compared to the quantity, size or number of another.

Radius: a straight line from the centre of a circle to any point on its circumference.

Range: the difference between the largest and smallest values in a data set.

Ratio: a way to compare (or show the relationship between) two or more quantities of the same kind.

Scale diagram: a proportional 2-D drawing of a real-life object.

Side elevation: a 2-D drawing of a 3-D shape as seen from the side of a shape.

Surface area: a measure of the total surface area of all the exterior parts of a shape. The units used for measuring surface area are m^2, cm^2, $inches^2$ etc.

Tree diagram: a clear way of recording all the possible outcomes of an event.

Two-way table: a table that shows the frequencies for two variables, with one being represented using rows and the other using columns.

Index